MULTILEVEL MATH FUN

Instant Games & Activities for the Multilevel Classroom

Written by
Dr. Carl Seltzer

Editor: Teri L. Fisch
Illustrator: Darcy Tom
Cover Illustrator: Rick Grayson
Designer: Moonhee Pak
Cover Designer: Moonhee Pak
Art Director: Tom Cochrane
Project Director: Carolea Williams

Table of Contents

Introduction 3
   Getting Started 4
   Organizing the Materials 5

NCTM Standards Correlation 6

Math Fun for the Whole Class
   Hundred Board Patterns 7
      Hundred Board Puzzles 8
      Multiplication Fact Books 8
      Multiple Multiples 9
      Hidden Pictures 9
      Shortcut to Add 10
      Corner Numbers 10
      Square Pattern 11
      3 Chips 11

Math Fun for Individuals
   Hidden Words 12
   A-Mazing Math Mazes 17
   Missing Operations 22
   Number Puzzles 27
   The Path 32
   Inkblot Puzzles 37
   Input/Output 42

Math Fun for Two Players
   Spin Big! 47
   Smallest Answer Path 52
   Frame It 57
   Factor It 62

Math Fun for Two or More Players
   Close to the Target 67
   Speed Wheel 72
   Fractions in a Row 77
   Score More 80

Manipulatives and Game Pieces
   Hundred Board 85
   Number Cards 86
   Spinners 87
   Smile Squares 89
   Fraction Cards 90
   Fraction Caller Cards 92
   Dice 93

Answers 94

Multilevel Math Fun 3–5 features games and activities designed to help students learn mathematical skills, problem-solving strategies, and critical thinking skills while having fun with math. Each game or activity includes directions and reproducibles for four different skill levels, with the least complex concepts first and the most complex last, which allows you to differentiate your math instruction to meet the needs of each student in your classroom. The math skills range from addition and subtraction to multiplication, long division, and negative numbers.

Choose from games and activities for the whole class, individuals, pairs, and small groups. Each game or activity begins with a teacher page that includes

- a short materials list with key math skills listed for each reproducible
- easy-to-follow directions for preparation and play
- helpful hints such as extension ideas and ways to foster student success

Use this information to introduce, set up, and implement each game or activity. Refer to the NCTM Standards Correlation chart (page 6) to identify the games and activities that focus on the specific skills and standards you want to target. This resource also features a variety of math manipulatives and game pieces and a handy answer key for the activities.

To extend learning, challenge students to modify the games or invent similar ones. Encourage them to create games at an appropriate level and write clear directions and rules. You will be amazed at the students' creativity and they will feel a sense of excitement as well as accomplishment when they see their classmates playing games they created!

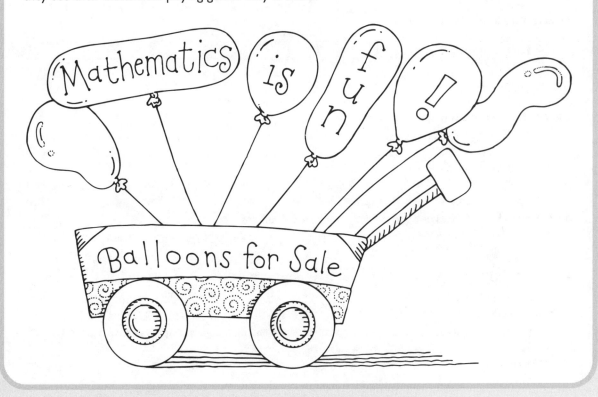

Getting Started

The math games and activities in this book provide a fun and easy way to differentiate curriculum. Model how to play each game before students begin to play it. The following descriptions explain how to use the games and activities from each section in your classroom of multilevel learners.

Math Fun for the Whole Class

Begin with the activities in this section, which all use the Hundred Board (page 85). The math concepts in these activities become progressively more difficult, but many of them can be adapted to meet your instructional needs. The activities will help you teach students how to use their hundred chart to practice math skills at different levels. Use the activities in this section to help you assess the math "comfort level" of your whole class and individual students.

Math Fun for Individuals

Students do not have to complete the activities in this section in sequence, but they should have the necessary prerequisite skills before they start each activity. Review the directions for each activity, choose the skill level you wish to target, and select a reproducible at that level for every student to complete or for students who finish other work early to complete. Another option is to choose an activity and invite students to complete some or all of the reproducibles over a given period of time. Since the four reproducibles for each activity get progressively more difficult, students will complete them at different speeds and some students may not have the necessary skills to handle the more complex concepts yet. You may also choose to introduce an activity to the whole class and then have students complete one or more of the reproducibles for homework, as class work, at a center, or as a combination of these.

Math Fun for Two Players

Choose a different game each week, explain the general rules to the whole class, and provide time during the week for students to play it. Keep the game at a math center. Have students play it when they have finished another math assignment, or have the whole class play in pairs at the same time. With the second option, the whole class plays the same game, but each pair of students plays at their own skill level. Assess students' math abilities by observing play at each level of the game. Once you feel a student has mastered one skill level, invite him or her to play the next level, and so on.

Math Fun for Two or More Players

Choose a different game each month, and teach the whole class or small groups of students how to play it. Then, have students play the game using the reproducible that addresses the math skill most appropriate to their skill level or the one that addresses the skills you want to target. Have groups of students play the game during center time, or divide the class into small groups and have the whole class play at the same time. Vary the reproducible students complete so that sometimes they start with the least complex concept (the first reproducible of a game) and at other times they start with the most complex one.

Organizing the Materials

Photocopy the reproducibles and game pieces on construction paper or card stock, and laminate them for durability. Have students use dry erase markers to write on the laminated materials so they can be used again and again. Place the materials for each game or activity in a large envelope or resealable plastic bag. Include a sheet that lists the name of the game or activity and a list of the materials. This makes it easy to keep track of the materials in each envelope or bag and you can quickly and easily hand them out to pairs or small groups of students. Encourage students to use manipulatives (e.g., linking cubes, poker chips) to keep score or to write tally marks on a piece of scratch paper.

The standards listed on the chart represent those identified by the National Council of Teachers of Mathematics. Use this chart to identify games and activities that address the standards you wish to reinforce.

	Numbers & Operations										
	Addition	Decimals	Division	Fractions	Multiplication	Negative integers	Percents	Subtraction	Algebra	Geometry	Problem solving
A-Mazing Math Mazes	X	X	X	X	X	X		X			
Close to the Target	X	X		X	X			X			X
Factor It					X						
Fractions in a Row				X							
Frame It	X	X	X	X	X		X	X			X
Hidden Words										X	
Hundred Board Patterns	X		X		X			X	X	X	X
Inkblot Puzzles	X	X	X	X	X	X		X	X		X
Input/Output	X		X		X			X	X		X
Missing Operations	X		X	X	X			X	X		X
Number Puzzles	X	X		X							X
The Path	X				X				X		X
Score More	X		X		X			X			X
Smallest Answer Path	X			X	X	X					X
Speed Wheel	X	X	X	X	X	X		X			
Spin Big!	X		X		X			X			

Hundred Board Patterns

Materials

✔ **Hundred Board**
  (page 85)
✔ **blank white paper**
✔ **stapler**

Helpful Hints

➤ Photocopy the Hundred Boards on card stock or construction paper, and laminate them. Have students use dry erase markers to write on their boards.

➤ Have students write their name or initials on their Hundred Board to help them find misplaced boards.

1 Give each student a Hundred Board. Review the numbers 1–100. Ask students to share patterns they see on the board. Have students keep their board in their desk, in a folder, or in a designated area. (Some activities require additional copies of the Hundred Board.)

2 Ask students to make a math journal by folding several pieces of blank white paper in half and stapling them on the paper fold. Have students write a title and their name (e.g., *My Math Explanations by Anita Tom*) on the front of their journal.

3 Ask students to write about each activity in this section in their math journal. Have them explain the pattern they created, how they figured it out, and how they would explain it to a classmate.

Hundred Board Puzzles »

Photocopy a class set of Hundred Boards, and give each student a reproducible. Invite students to cut apart their board on the lines between numbers to create 10–20 "puzzle pieces." Tell students to place their pieces in an envelope and label it *Hundred Board Puzzle Created by* _____. Have students trade envelopes with a partner. Set a timer, and challenge partners to put together each other's puzzles within a set time (e.g., 3–5 minutes). Ask students to trade puzzles and repeat this activity several times.

Materials

✔ **Hundred Board**
(page 85)
COUNTING, PATTERNS, VISUAL DISCRIMINATION

✔ **scissors**

✔ **envelopes**

✔ **timer**

« Multiplication Fact Books

Materials

✔ **Hundred Board**
(page 85)
(13 for each small group)
MULTIPLICATION, MULTIPLES AND FACTORS, PATTERNS

✔ **graph paper** (optional)

✔ **colored pencils**

✔ **math journals**

✔ **construction paper**

✔ **hole punch**

✔ **yarn**

Invite students to make multiplication fact books. Divide the class into small groups. Give each group 13 Hundred Boards. (Photocopy pages back-to-back to save paper, or give students graph paper and invite them to make their own hundred boards.) Tell students to label each page *Multiples of ___* and color in the multiples for each number from 0 to 12. Have groups discuss each pattern they created and write about it in their math journals. Then, have volunteers discuss each pattern with the class. Invite students to use construction paper to make front and back covers, hole-punch all their pages, and then bind together their book by tieing yarn through the holes. Have them write *Multiplication Fact Book 0–12* on the cover. Store the books in the classroom library.

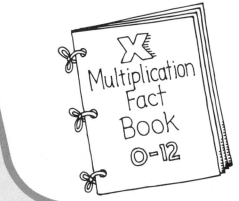

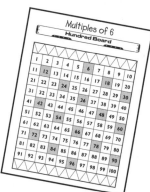

Multiple Multiples

Divide the class into small groups. Give each group three different colors of counting chips, linking cubes, or another small manipulative. (Provide at least 50 of each color.) Tell each group to use one student's Hundred Board. Invite students to cover on their board all multiples of 2 with one color and all multiples of 3 with a second color. Ask students to identify which numbers are covered by two colors and explain in their math journal why these numbers are covered by both. Encourage them to share their responses with the class. Have students record in their math journal the multiples of each number. Have groups clear their board and repeat this activity with two new numbers and then add a third.

Materials

✔ **Hundred Board**
(page 85)
MULTIPLICATION, MULTIPLES, PRIME NUMBERS

✔ **counting chips, linking cubes, or small manipulatives** (3 colors for each group)

✔ **math journals**

Hidden Pictures

Cut apart construction paper squares large enough to cover the boxes on the Hundred Board. Have students use their own Hundred Board for this activity. Give each student a set of nine squares and a piece of scratch paper. Write on the board the problems shown below. Have students complete them and cover each answer on their Hundred Board with a paper square. When they are through, they will see a capital T.

Materials

✔ **Hundred Board**
(page 85)
ADDITION, SUBTRACTION, MULTIPLICATION, DIVISION, VISUAL DISCRIMINATION

✔ **construction paper**
✔ **scratch paper**

Solve these problems. Cover your answers on your Hundred Board.

$7 + (7 \times 4)$	$(100 \div 4) + 1$	$(78 - 30) \div 2$
$(10 \times 3) - 3$	$(13 \times 10) \div 2$	$2 \times (8 + 11) + 7$
$(80 - 20) \div 2 + (10 + 15)$	$9 + (9 + 9) - 4$	$2 \times (3 + 5) + 9$

Challenge students to work in small groups to create their own puzzles to exchange with other groups. Have students create problems with a specific operation (e.g., 3-digit multiplication) or a combination of operations.

Shortcut to Add

Challenge students to work independently or with a partner to add all 100 numbers on their Hundred Board using as many patterns and shortcuts as they can find. (The correct sum is 5,050.) Invite students to record in their math journal their equations and explain how they calculated their answer. Challenge students to find the shortest way to find the answer in the shortest amount of time.

Materials

✔ **Hundred Board**
(page 85)
ADDITION, MULTIPLICATION, PROBLEM SOLVING

✔ **math journals**

Corner Numbers

Invite students to use colored pencils to circle or lightly shade the four numbers on the corners of their Hundred Board (i.e., 1, 10, 91, and 100). Challenge students to be the first person to figure out what the relationship is between these four numbers. Have students write in their math journal the relationship in equation form. Ask them to explain how they figured it out.

Materials

✔ **Hundred Board**
(page 85)
PROBLEM SOLVING, ALGEBRA

✔ **colored pencils**
✔ **math journals**

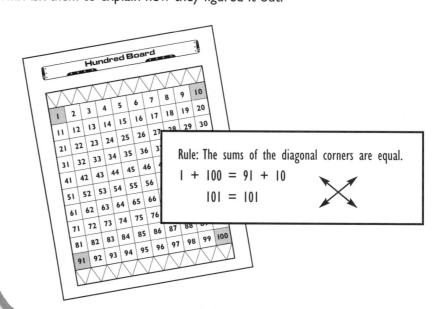

Square Pattern

Divide the class into small groups. Have each group use one student's Hundred Board. Ask groups to use a colored pencil or dry erase marker to draw a square around any four numbers (e.g., 9, 10, 19, 20) on their board. Have students come up with a rule that describes the relationship between these four numbers. Encourage groups to draw squares around four different sets of numbers so they can compare them to make sure their rule works. (Hint: The rule involves addition.) Challenge students to discover if this rule always works. Have each student explain why in his or her math journal.

> The sums along each diagonal are the same (29).
> If $9 = a$, then you have: $a, a + 1, a + 10, a + 11$
> Therefore, $a + (a + 11) = (a + 10) + (a + 1)$
> or $2a + 11 = 2a + 11$

Materials

✔ **Hundred Board**
(page 85)
PROBLEM SOLVING, ALGEBRA, PATTERNS

✔ **colored pencils or dry erase markers**

✔ **math journals**

---

3 Chips

Materials

✔ **Hundred Board**
(page 85)
PROBLEM SOLVING, ALGEBRA

✔ **counting chips**

✔ **math journals**

Divide the class into small groups. Give each group nine counting chips, and tell each group to use one student's Hundred Board. Have groups place three counting chips over any three numbers that touch in a straight line horizontally, vertically, or diagonally (e.g., 3, 4, 5 or 7, 17, 27 or 13, 22, 31). Encourage groups to do this for three different sets of numbers so they can compare them. Ask students to look carefully at the three numbers, determine the relationship between these numbers, and write in their math journal an algebraic rule for this relationship. (Hint: The rule involves addition and multiplication.) Have students extend their rule and explanation by writing a rule for the pattern or relationship that exists for five, seven, and nine numbers in a row. Challenge groups to tell whether their rule can be applied to any set of numbers or only a certain set of numbers.

| 3 | 4 | 5 |

> If M = middle #, the one before M = M − 1 and the one after M = M + 1. Therefore,
> $(M − 1) + M + (M + 1) = 3M$
>
> *Rule: The sum of any 3 numbers in a row always equals 3 times the middle number.

Hidden Words

Levels

✔ **reproducibles (choose the appropriate level)**

1 •••••••••••• ● Find Equation Words (page 13)
MATH VOCABULARY: NUMBERS & OPERATIONS (15 WORDS)

2 •••••••••••• ● Find Number Words (page 14)
MATH VOCABULARY: PLACE VALUE (20 WORDS)

3 •••••••••••• ● Find Math Words (page 15)
MATH VOCABULARY (30 WORDS)

4 •••••••••••• ● Find Geometry Words (page 16)
MATH VOCABULARY: GEOMETRY (35 WORDS)

✔ **dictionaries or math textbooks**

✔ **math journals**

Directions

1 Give each student a reproducible at the appropriate level.

2 Invite students to complete their activity by circling or lightly shading the hidden words.

3 Give each student a dictionary or tell students to use the glossary in their math book. Have students write in their math journal a definition and an example for five to ten of the hidden words in their puzzle.

4 Invite volunteers to share their definitions and examples.

Helpful Hints

➤ Tell students to first read through all the words hidden in the puzzle and then look at one row at a time. Encourage students to choose a hidden word and look only for the letter that word begins with until they find the whole word.

➤ Encourage students to circle, cross out, or put a check next to words as they find them.

➤ Make an overhead transparency of a reproducible, and give each student a paper copy. Invite students to find the hidden words on their paper and then circle them on the transparency.

Name_____ Date _____

Find Equation Words

There are 15 words hidden in the puzzle **horizontally** and **vertically**.
Can you find all of them? Circle or lightly shade the words as you find them.

A	B	N	F	C	S	U	M	S	B
W	K	U	A	J	F	D	I	O	P
D	V	M	C	F	R	S	R	L	R
S	U	B	T	R	A	C	T	V	O
L	G	E	O	H	C	Q	P	E	B
Y	U	R	R	A	T	I	O	A	L
Q	L	F	S	D	I	V	I	D	E
U	A	G	T	D	O	Y	K	W	M
O	N	T	I	I	N	D	F	B	E
T	S	E	M	T	Y	D	N	C	Q
I	W	S	U	I	C	X	J	Z	U
E	E	P	R	O	D	U	C	T	A
N	R	Q	H	N	P	G	M	O	L
T	M	U	L	T	I	P	L	Y	S

ADDITION	FACTOR	PROBLEM	SOLVE
ANSWER	FRACTION	PRODUCT	SUBTRACT
DIVIDE	MULTIPLY	QUOTIENT	SUM
EQUALS	NUMBER	RATIO	

Name_____   Date _____

Find Number Words

There are 20 words hidden in the puzzle **horizontally**, **vertically**, and **diagonally**.
Can you find all of them? Circle or lightly shade the words as you find them.

Z	E	R	O	N	V	Q	U	A	R	T	E	R	F
A	R	P	B	Q	U	B	I	L	L	I	O	N	G
H	D	D	L	C	F	M	F	I	N	H	T	T	E
U	C	C	P	A	H	Z	E	O	S	J	H	H	R
N	E	O	T	G	C	S	S	R	M	D	I	O	T
D	S	M	M	W	U	E	V	O	A	K	R	U	H
R	C	P	E	M	I	P	V	S	N	L	D	S	O
E	B	A	B	V	A	C	Z	A	W	M	I	A	U
D	P	R	K	R	U	T	Q	T	L	J	O	N	S
T	T	E	N	P	P	R	M	P	Y	U	N	D	A
H	E	Z	A	H	U	N	D	R	E	D	E	T	N
S	N	O	L	D	E	C	I	M	A	L	S	H	D
D	T	Z	X	N	C	T	D	I	G	I	T	S	Y
F	H	A	E	U	M	I	L	L	I	O	N	S	A
C	S	Y	V	G	D	U	Z	L	J	K	H	O	N
H	A	L	F	I	N	U	M	B	E	R	M	G	W

BILLION	HALF	NUMERAL	TENTHS
COMMA	HUNDRED	ONES	THIRD
COMPARE	HUNDREDTHS	PLACE VALUE	THOUSAND
DECIMAL	MILLIONS	QUARTER	THOUSANDTHS
DIGITS	NUMBER	TEN	ZERO

Multilevel Math Fun • 3–5 © 2002 Creative Teaching Press

Find Math Words

Name_____   Date _____

Multilevel Math Fun • 3–5 © 2002 Creative Teaching Press

Directions

There are 30 words hidden in the puzzle **horizontally, vertically, diagonally,** and **backwards.** Can you find all of them? Circle or lightly shade the words as you find them.

A	E	C	D	Y	W	D	I	F	F	E	R	E	N	C	E	P
B	E	Q	U	A	T	I	O	N	A	X	E	N	P	F	C	X
K	T	U	S	B	B	G	D	D	E	C	I	M	A	L	O	M
V	G	Y	M	U	D	I	V	I	D	E	N	D	Z	G	M	N
A	E	G	U	R	M	T	A	M	H	I	J	I	D	H	P	P
Z	P	R	O	B	A	B	I	L	I	T	Y	V	Y	U	U	Q
H	O	F	P	G	X	C	L	Q	U	O	T	I	E	N	T	Z
I	S	H	P	R	I	M	E	A	A	P	O	S	V	D	A	E
J	I	S	O	M	V	W	Q	P	T	Z	M	I	B	R	T	O
L	T	R	S	T	W	N	O	S	R	O	Z	O	M	E	I	R
I	I	D	I	V	I	S	O	R	O	M	T	N	I	D	O	Y
H	V	G	T	Q	F	F	N	E	G	A	T	I	V	E	N	L
X	E	D	E	N	O	M	I	N	A	T	O	R	L	T	K	Q
U	T	H	O	U	S	A	N	D	E	F	I	L	D	V	I	S
V	O	O	M	B	O	S	I	I	B	R	E	S	T	R	K	D
A	D	E	M	A	N	I	P	U	L	A	T	I	V	E	J	R
K	M	A	A	G	O	B	S	S	U	C	F	V	G	M	H	T
M	U	L	T	I	P	L	I	C	A	T	I	O	N	A	C	B
C	L	G	H	B	E	Q	U	A	L	I	D	L	F	I	B	G
S	T	E	N	O	R	C	Z	K	V	O	Q	W	R	N	O	U
R	I	B	D	Z	C	W	M	A	T	N	S	I	P	D	N	H
C	P	R	A	F	E	S	T	I	M	A	T	E	S	E	B	J
D	L	A	B	A	N	O	O	N	V	L	M	K	Q	R	W	V
E	E	W	X	G	T	H	Y	J	K	Y	R	O	T	C	A	F

ALGEBRA	DIVIDEND	FACTOR	MULTIPLICATION	PROBABILITY
COMPUTATION	DIVISION	FRACTION	NEGATIVE	QUOTIENT
DECIMAL	DIVISOR	HUNDRED	OPPOSITE	REMAINDER
DENOMINATOR	EQUAL	MANIPULATIVE	PERCENT	SUM
DIFFERENCE	EQUATION	MATH	POSITIVE	THOUSAND
DIGIT	ESTIMATE	MULTIPLE	PRIME	TOTAL

Find Geometry Words

Directions

There are 35 words hidden in the puzzle **horizontally, vertically, diagonally,** and **backwards.** Can you find all of them? Circle or lightly shade the words as you find them.

T	C	A	F	B	G	E	O	M	E	T	R	Y	M	N	O	N
R	H	O	M	B	U	S	I	K	G	R	A	P	H	P	R	T
A	O	E	A	B	L	D	H	I	J	I	S	A	E	R	A	O
P	R	D	A	C	G	B	S	T	P	A	W	X	X	A	B	C
E	D	E	U	C	S	Q	P	L	A	N	E	P	A	X	I	S
Z	S	E	V	W	U	B	V	R	U	G	E	G	G	Q	D	P
O	T	F	W	A	T	J	E	P	T	L	F	S	O	L	I	D
I	E	D	R	S	R	T	C	U	B	E	O	R	N	S	K	E
D	F	E	Y	T	E	G	I	X	F	O	Z	N	G	M	L	B
E	G	E	F	M	F	B	R	Z	Y	N	T	R	P	S	T	K
R	F	T	A	G	H	O	C	E	N	T	E	R	R	A	Y	T
C	D	I	E	E	X	A	L	M	M	Y	K	L	I	N	E	U
A	D	R	Y	M	A	N	E	Y	N	U	J	L	S	I	D	E
H	P	A	R	A	L	L	E	L	O	G	R	A	M	B	T	M
Y	Y	Q	A	B	C	P	Y	X	C	Z	H	W	B	J	V	U
T	R	A	D	I	U	S	I	N	T	E	R	S	E	C	T	L
I	A	N	B	Q	I	M	U	N	A	I	C	W	B	O	C	O
C	M	G	H	P	E	N	T	A	G	O	N	A	D	O	D	V
A	I	L	R	K	C	L	L	H	O	G	E	X	N	L	L	C
P	D	E	W	S	E	G	M	E	N	T	D	E	E	W	G	O
A	A	I	U	E	T	A	F	G	S	S	P	H	E	R	E	N
C	O	O	R	D	I	N	A	T	E	L	N	L	M	N	O	P
C	K	Q	R	S	J	O	P	C	K	O	P	R	A	U	V	W
F	B	C	E	H	I	L	S	T	A	P	Q	E	B	F	M	D
G	Q	U	A	D	R	I	L	A	T	E	R	A	L	C	G	H

ANGLE	CONE	INTERSECT	PYRAMID	SLOPE
AREA	COORDINATE	LINE	QUADRILATERAL	SOLID
AXIS	CUBE	OCTAGON	RADIUS	SPHERE
CAPACITY	DIAMETER	PARALLELOGRAM	RAY	SQUARE
CENTER	GEOMETRY	PENTAGON	RHOMBUS	TRAPEZOID
CHORD	GRAPH	PLANE	SEGMENT	TRIANGLE
CIRCLE	HEXAGON	PRISM	SIDE	VOLUME

Multilevel Math Fun • 3–5 © 2002 Creative Teaching Press

A-Mazing Math Mazes

Levels

✔ **reproducibles (choose the appropriate level)**

1 ● Number Maze (page 18)
ADDITION, SUBTRACTION, MULTIPLICATION, DIVISION

2 ● Decimal Maze (page 19)
ADDITION, SUBTRACTION, MULTIPLICATION, AND DIVISION OF DECIMALS

3 ● Negative and Positive Maze (page 20)
ADDITION AND SUBTRACTION OF NEGATIVE AND POSITIVE INTEGERS

4 ● Fraction Maze (page 21)
ADDITION, SUBTRACTION, MULTIPLICATION, AND DIVISION OF FRACTIONS

Directions

1 Give each student a reproducible at the appropriate level.

2 Tell students to follow the math maze from "Start" to "End" with their finger.

3 Have them begin at the word *Start* and solve the problems as they go through the maze path to the word *End*.

4 Invite students to write their final answer in the star burst at the end of the maze.

Helpful Hints

➤ Encourage students to compute each problem along the maze path on scratch paper and then record their answer on the side of the maze.

➤ Invite students to check their final answer with a calculator.

➤ Use correction fluid to delete the numbers on the mazes. (Leave the operation symbols.) Laminate the reproducibles. Invite students to use dry erase markers to write numbers in the boxes and complete their maze or have a classmate complete it.

Name_____ Date _____

Number Maze

Directions

Follow the math maze from "Start" to "End." Solve the addition, subtraction, multiplication, and division problems as you go. Write the final answer in the star burst.

I'm ready to start!

7	÷	3		7	+	7
÷		–		÷		×
3		8		4		5
+		×		–		÷
8		3		6		3
–		÷		×		×
6		6		8		4
+		–		+		–
7		3		10		3
=		+		÷		+
		4	×	6		6
						Start

End

Multilevel Math Fun • 3–5 © 2002 Creative Teaching Press

Decimal Maze

Directions

Follow the math maze from "Start" to "End." Solve the addition, subtraction, multiplication, and division problems as you go. Write the final answer in the star burst.

Start						
3.2		0.1	−	38.9		
+		×		÷		
6.8		0.1		2.0	1.26	=
×		÷		+	−	
0.6		69.8		8.4	0.8	
−		−		−	×	
1.4		4.2		4.2	0.1	
÷		×		×	+	
2.0		4.6		0.2	2.3	
−		+		+	+	
2.2	+	32.8		6.2	−	9.62

End

Multilevel Math Fun • 3–5 © 2002 Creative Teaching Press

Name_____   Date _____

Negative and Positive Maze

Multilevel Math Fun • 3–5 © 2002 Creative Teaching Press

Directions

Follow the math maze from "Start" to "End."
Solve the addition and subtraction problems as
you go. Write the final answer in the star burst.

						Start
=	−9		+4	−	−8	+10
	+		−		+	−
	−8		−1		−2	+3
	−		+		−	+
	+4		−6		+6	−7
	+		+		−	+
	+5		+2		+8	−5
	−		−		+	−
	0	+	−9		+6	+	−2

End

Name_____ Date _____

Fraction Maze

Directions

Follow the math maze from "Start" to "End." Solve the addition,
subtraction, multiplication, and division problems as you go. Remember
to reduce your fractions as you solve problems. (It will make your
maze path easier.) Write the final answer in the star burst.

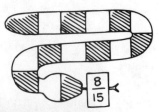

$1\frac{3}{4}$	÷	$\frac{1}{2}$			
+		+			
$\frac{1}{6}$		$\frac{9}{2}$			
−		−			
$\frac{2}{6}$		$\frac{1}{3}$		$4\frac{1}{8}$	=
×		÷		−	
$\frac{1}{4}$		$\frac{1}{6}$		5	
+		−		÷	
$\frac{1}{4}$		$\frac{3}{3}$	×	$2\frac{1}{9}$	
Start					

End

Missing Operations

Levels

✔ **reproducibles (choose the appropriate level)**

1 • Owl Operations (page 23)
2-STEP PROBLEM SOLVING (ALGEBRA WITH WHOLE NUMBERS)

2 • Fox Operations (page 24)
1- TO 3-STEP PROBLEM SOLVING (ALGEBRA WITH WHOLE NUMBERS AND FRACTIONS)

3 • Crocodile Operations (page 25)
3- TO 4-STEP PROBLEM SOLVING (ALGEBRA WITH WHOLE NUMBERS AND FRACTIONS)

4 • Lobster Operations (page 26)
2- TO 5-STEP PROBLEM SOLVING (ALGEBRA WITH WHOLE NUMBERS AND FRACTIONS)

✔ **scratch paper**

✔ **calculators (optional)**

« Directions

1 Give each student a reproducible at the appropriate level and a piece of scratch paper.

2 Tell students to fill in each blank box with an operation symbol that makes each equation correct.

3 Encourage them to work out each problem on their scratch paper.

4 Have students check their work by completing the entire problem after they have written operation symbols in the blank boxes. (Invite students who need help to use a calculator to help them as they solve the problems.)

Helpful Hints

➤ Tell students that each page has equations with addition, subtraction, multiplication, and division. (For some problems that include fractions, students will need to reduce their final answer.)

➤ Invite students to cut out 14 paper squares and label them with the numbers 0–9 and operation symbols (+, −, x, ÷). Have students use the number squares to create an equation from their paper and then try different operation symbols in the equation as they try to solve it.

Name_____   Date _____

Owl Operations

Fill in each blank box with an operation symbol (+, −, x, or ÷) to make each equation correct.

1. 8 ☐ 2 ☐ 9 = 1

2. 4 ☐ 4 ☐ 8 = 2

3. 3 ☐ 3 ☐ 3 = 3

4. 16 ☐ 4 ☐ 3 = 4

5. 20 ☐ 2 ☐ 5 = 5

6. 15 ☐ 5 ☐ 4 = 6

7. 5 ☐ 5 ☐ 18 = 7

8. 2 ☐ 4 ☐ 1 = 8

9. 4 ☐ 4 ☐ 7 = 9

10. 15 ☐ 3 ☐ 5 = 10

Name_____   Date _____

Fox Operations

Fill in each blank box with an operation symbol (+, −, x, or ÷) to make each equation correct.

1. 20 ☐ 20 ☐ 5 = 395

2. 6 ☐ 6 ☐ 6 ☐ 6 = 48

3. $\frac{1}{2}$ ☐ $\frac{1}{3}$ = $\frac{1}{6}$

4. $\frac{1}{2}$ ☐ $\frac{1}{3}$ = $\frac{3}{2}$

5. $\frac{1}{3}$ ☐ $\frac{1}{2}$ = $\frac{2}{3}$

6. $\frac{1}{2}$ ☐ $\frac{1}{3}$ = $\frac{5}{6}$

7. 36 ☐ 6 ☐ 3 ☐ 9 = 0

8. 4444 ☐ 444 ☐ 44 = 4044

9. 4 ☐ 4 ☐ 4 ☐ 4 = 60

10. $\frac{1}{2}$ ☐ $\frac{1}{3}$ ☐ $\frac{1}{4}$ = $\frac{7}{12}$

Multilevel Math Fun • 3–5 © 2002 Creative Teaching Press

Crocodile Operations

Directions

Fill in each blank box with an operation symbol (+, −, x, or ÷) to make each equation correct.

1. $\frac{1}{4}$ ☐ $\frac{1}{4}$ ☐ $\frac{1}{4}$ ☐ $\frac{1}{2}$ = $\frac{1}{4}$

2. 4 ☐ (4 ☐ 4) ☐ 4 = 5

3. ($\frac{2}{7}$ ☐ $\frac{7}{2}$) − ($\frac{3}{5}$ ☐ $\frac{5}{3}$) = 0

4. 2 ☐ 3 ☐ $\frac{1}{2}$ ☐ 9 = 12

5. 10 ☐ 10 ☐ 10 ☐ 10 = 1

6. (100 ☐ 94) x (6 ☐ 3) = 108

7. $\frac{1}{3}$ x 9 ☐ 4 ☐ 6 ☐ 3 = 39

8. (14 ☐ 5) ÷ (7 ☐ 0) = 10

9. $\frac{1}{2}$ ☐ 3 ☐ $\frac{1}{6}$ ☐ 4 = 1

10. 4 ☐ 4 ☐ 4 − (4 ☐ 4) = 11

Multilevel Math Fun • 3–5 © 2002 Creative Teaching Press

Name_____   Date _____

Lobster Operations

Directions

Fill in each blank box with an operation symbol (+, −, x, or ÷) to make each equation correct.

1. $\dfrac{3}{8}$ ☐ $\dfrac{1}{2}$ ☐ $\dfrac{1}{4}$ = $\dfrac{5}{8}$

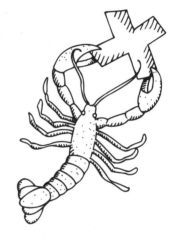

2. $\dfrac{2}{3}$ ☐ $\dfrac{1}{6}$ ☐ $\dfrac{2}{3}$ ☐ $\dfrac{1}{3}$ = $\dfrac{1}{2}$

3. (3 ☐ 5) + (4 ☐ 6) ☐ 3 = 13

4. [$\dfrac{1}{2}$ ☐ (4 ☐ 2)] × [$\dfrac{1}{3}$ ☐ (4 ☐ 2)] = 6

5. ($\dfrac{3}{8}$ ☐ $\dfrac{1}{2}$) + ($\dfrac{3}{8}$ ☐ $\dfrac{1}{2}$) = $\dfrac{15}{16}$

6. $\dfrac{3}{2}$ ☐ $\dfrac{1}{3}$ ☐ $\dfrac{2}{3}$ ☐ $\dfrac{1}{2}$ = 3

7. $\dfrac{1}{2}$ ☐ $\dfrac{3}{16}$ ☐ $\dfrac{1}{8}$ = $\dfrac{3}{16}$

8. ($\dfrac{2}{3}$ ☐ $\dfrac{1}{3}$) ÷ ($\dfrac{2}{3}$ ☐ $\dfrac{1}{2}$) = $\dfrac{6}{7}$

9. ($\dfrac{1}{5}$ ☐ $\dfrac{2}{5}$) − ($\dfrac{3}{5}$ ☐ $\dfrac{4}{5}$) = $\dfrac{3}{25}$

10. $\dfrac{2}{3}$ ☐ ($\dfrac{1}{2}$ × $\dfrac{2}{3}$) ☐ $\dfrac{1}{2}$ = $\dfrac{1}{2}$

Multilevel Math Fun • 3–5 © 2002 Creative Teaching Press

Number Puzzles

Materials

Levels

✔ **reproducibles (choose the appropriate level)**

1 • Sums of 9 (page 28)
    PROBLEM SOLVING WITH ADDITION

2 • Sums of 15 (page 29)
    PROBLEM SOLVING WITH ADDITION

3 • Sums of 1½ (page 30)
    PROBLEM SOLVING WITH ADDITION OF FRACTIONS

4 • Sums of 2.1 (page 31)
    PROBLEM SOLVING WITH ADDITION OF DECIMALS

✔ **Number Cards** (page 86)

✔ **resealable plastic bags (1 for each student)**

Directions

1 Cut apart a set of Number Cards for each player, and store each set in a separate bag.

2 Give each student a reproducible at the appropriate level and a bag of cards.

3 Have students read the directions at the top of their paper to see what numbers they will be using. Have them take those number cards out of their bag.

4 Invite students to place their number cards in the squares so that the sum in every connected straight line equals the target sum on their paper.

5 Tell students to explain on the lines at the bottom of their paper the strategy they used to solve the puzzle.

Helpful Hints

➤ When you cut apart the Number Cards, separate them into plastic bags for each puzzle. (Each reproducible lists the numbers students will need.) If you do this, you can skip step 3 of the directions, which will lessen the chance that students will use the wrong cards and not be able to solve their puzzle.

➤ Have students check each line of their puzzle by adding together the numbers and writing the sum on the line that connects the boxes.

Name _____   Date _____

Sums of 9

Place the numbers **0, 1, 2, 3, 4, 5,** and **6** in the squares so that the sum of the numbers in every connected straight line equals **9.**

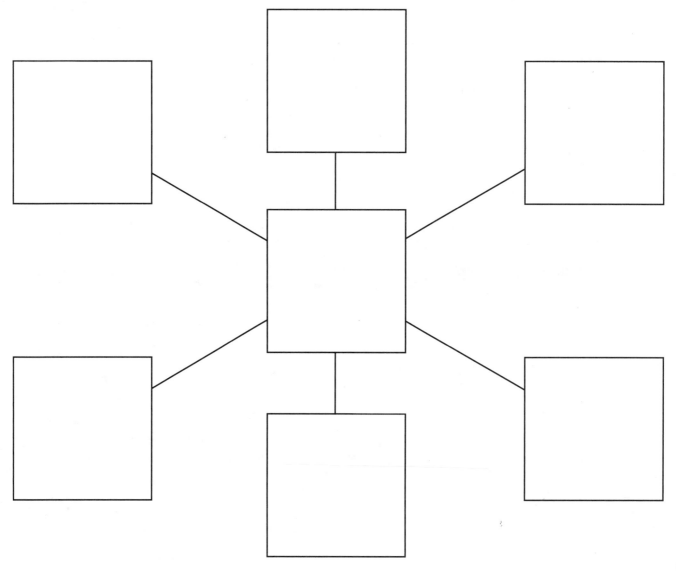

Explain your strategy.

_____

_____

_____

Name_____   Date_____

Sums of 15

Multilevel Math Fun • 3–5 © 2002 Creative Teaching Press

Directions

Place the numbers **2, 3, 4, 5, 6, 7,** and **8** in the squares so that the sum of the numbers in every connected straight line equals **15.**

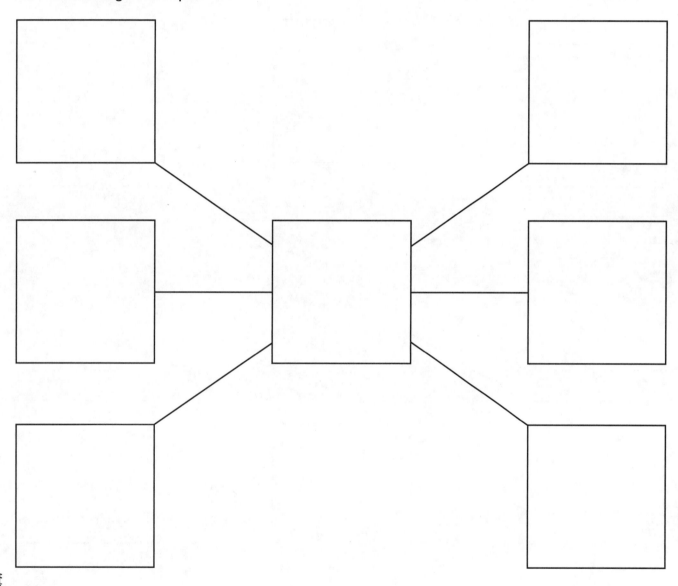

Explain your strategy.

_____

_____

_____

_____

Sums of 1½

Directions

Place the fractions $\frac{1}{10}$, $\frac{2}{10}$, $\frac{3}{10}$, $\frac{4}{10}$, $\frac{5}{10}$, $\frac{6}{10}$, $\frac{7}{10}$, $\frac{8}{10}$, and $\frac{9}{10}$ in the squares so that the sum of the numbers in every connected straight line equals $1\frac{1}{2}$.

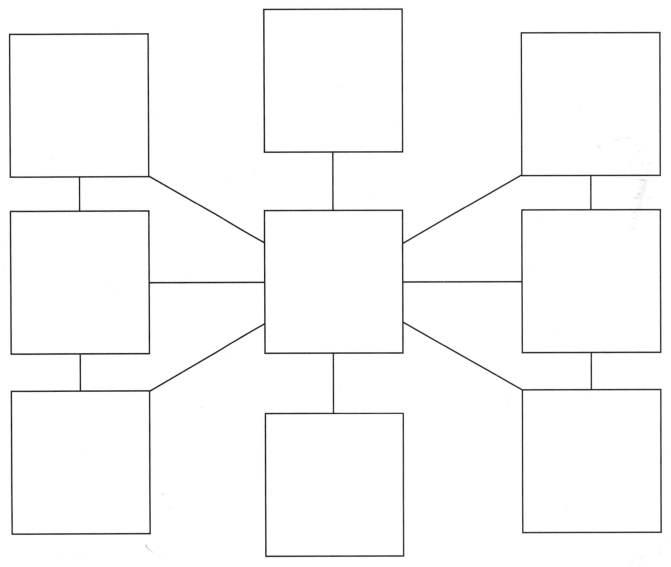

Explain your strategy.

_____

_____

_____

Multilevel Math Fun • 3–5 © 2002 Creative Teaching Press

Name_____   Date _____

Sums of 2.1

Directions

Place the decimals **0.3, 0.4, 0.5, 0.6, 0.7, 0.8, 0.9, 1.0,** and **1.1** in the squares so that the sum of the numbers in every connected straight line equals **2.1.**

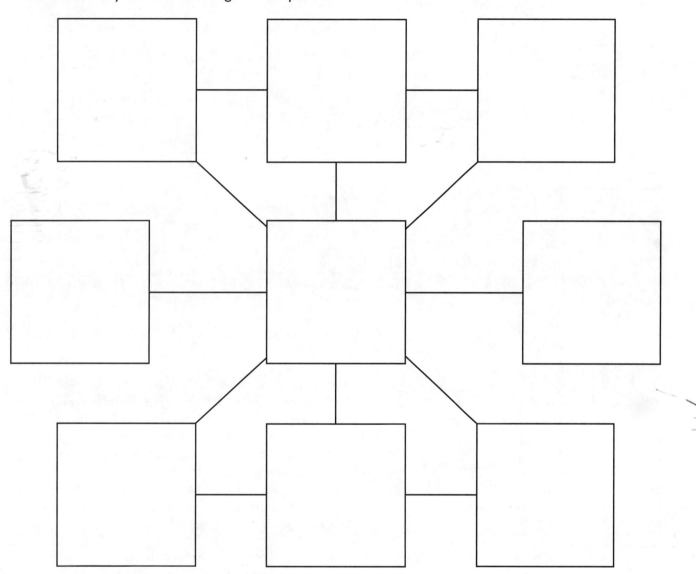

Explain your strategy.

_____

_____

_____

_____

The Path

Materials

Levels

✔ **reproducibles (choose the appropriate level)**

1 ● Ship's Path to 50 (page 33)
  PROBLEM SOLVING, ADDITION

2 ● Train's Path to 100 (page 34)
  PROBLEM SOLVING, ADDITION

3 ● Car's Path to 864 (page 35)
  PROBLEM SOLVING, MULTIPLICATION

4 ● Helicopter's Path to 1,296 (page 36)
  PROBLEM SOLVING, MULTIPLICATION

✔ **scratch paper**

Directions

1 Give each student a reproducible at the appropriate level and a piece of scratch paper.

2 Have students identify the target number on their paper. Tell students that they need to find a path through 14 numbers by adding or multiplying (depending on the reproducible) that equals the target number on their paper. Have them begin at the number below the word "Start" and connect a path through 14 numbers by drawing a line or lightly shading the boxes until they reach the number above the word "End." (Note: The path follows straight lines vertically and horizontally, not diagonally.) Encourage students to compute their answers on the scratch paper.

3 Have students complete the sentence at the bottom of their paper by writing a number sentence with the numbers along their path (e.g., 6 x 4 x 3 x 2 x 1 = 144).

Helpful Hints

➤ Tell students to lightly draw a line with their pencil along the paths they try until they find the correct one, and then have them darken it or shade the boxes. Or, laminate the reproducibles, and have students write on them with dry erase markers.

➤ Challenge students to race against other students or use a stopwatch to see who can correctly complete the path the fastest.

➤ Invite students to check their answers with a calculator.

Name_____ Date _____

Ship's Path to 50

Directions

Help the ship sail to its port. Begin at the number under "Start." Find the path through 14 numbers that add up to the **sum** of **50.** End at the number above "End." (Note: The path follows straight lines vertically and horizontally, not diagonally.) Write an addition sentence with the numbers you added together.

Start

3	2	3	4	5	6	7
6	2	4	0	3	2	1
9	3	6	4	0	1	2
4	5	2	1	5	6	7
3	2	4	3	9	9	8
4	7	6	7	2	1	4
9	7	5	1	4	3	0
2	1	3	2	3	4	2
4	3	6	3	9	7	5
7	2	4	4	0	5	9
2	4	1	0	6	0	8

End
50

The number path I took to find the sum of 50 was

_____.

Name_____   Date _____

Train's Path to 100

Directions

Help the train travel to the town of Toosey. Begin at the number under "Start." Find the path through 14 numbers that add up to the **sum** of **100.** End at the number above "End." (Note: The path follows straight lines vertically and horizontally, not diagonally.) Write an addition sentence with the numbers you added together.

Start

2	4	5	3	6	7	4
1	5	6	2	1	5	6
1	3	8	2	3	4	7
4	8	5	4	5	6	8
3	2	7	7	8	3	2
3	7	6	5	9	4	1
2	1	4	0	7	5	6
0	1	2	3	6	5	7
4	3	2	2	7	9	8
1	2	3	2	1	5	8

End

Toosey
100

The number path I took to find the sum of 100 was

_____.

Multilevel Math Fun • 3–5 © 2002 Creative Teaching Press

Name_____   Date _____

Car's Path to 864

Directions

Help the car find its way home. Begin at the number under "Start." Find the path through 14 numbers that when multiplied together equal the **product** of **864.** End at the number above "End." (Note: The path follows straight lines vertically and horizontally, not diagonally.) Write a multiplication sentence with the numbers you multiplied together.

Start

6	7	1	1	2	6	0
8	4	3	0	7	1	9
9	3	1	3	4	8	3
0	2	1	6	7	8	7
5	2	7	7	6	2	9
3	1	1	2	9	0	4
3	6	6	5	0	7	6
2	8	3	4	5	5	3
2	1	4	9	8	2	3

End

864

The number path I took to find the product of 864 was

_____.

Multilevel Math Fun • 3-5 © 2002 Creative Teaching Press

Math Fun for Individuals **35**

Name_____   Date _____

Helicopter's Path to 1,296

Directions

Help the helicopter locate its landing zone. Begin at the number under "Start." Find the path through 14 numbers that when multiplied together equal the **product** of **1,296.** End at the number above "End." (Note: The path follows straight lines vertically and horizontally, not diagonally.) Write a multiplication sentence with the numbers you multiplied together.

Start

6	4	3	4	1	3	1
1	2	5	3	2	1	2
0	2	4	0	1	3	4
3	2	1	6	3	2	1
3	5	1	3	3	5	0
6	4	0	2	1	3	4
2	1	3	2	4	1	3
3	1	4	1	3	2	1
4	5	3	2	3	2	0

End
1,296

The number path I took to find the product of 1,296 was

_____

Multilevel Math Fun • 3–5 © 2002 Creative Teaching Press

Inkblot Puzzles

Levels

✓ **reproducibles (choose the appropriate level)**

1 ● Ink Drips (page 38)
ALGEBRA, ADDITION, SUBTRACTION

2 ● Ink Spots (page 39)
ALGEBRA; ADDITION, SUBTRACTION, AND MULTIPLICATION OF WHOLE NUMBERS & FRACTIONS

3 ● Ink Stains (page 40)
ALGEBRA; ADDITION, SUBTRACTION, MULTIPLICATION, AND DIVISION OF WHOLE NUMBERS & FRACTIONS

4 ● Ink Splotches (page 41)
ALGEBRA; ADDITION, SUBTRACTION, MULTIPLICATION, AND DIVISION OF FRACTIONS, DECIMALS, AND POSITIVE AND NEGATIVE INTEGERS

✓ **scratch paper**

Directions

1 Give each student a reproducible at the appropriate level and a piece of scratch paper.

2 Tell students to fill in each inkblot with a number that makes each equation correct.

3 Encourage them to work out each problem on their scratch paper.

4 Have students check their work by completing the entire problem after they have written numbers in the blank spaces.

Helpful Hints

➤ Have students write the answer to each part of the problem as they fill in numbers to help them see if the numbers they have chosen are correct.

➤ Invite struggling students to use a calculator to help them as they solve the problems.

➤ Encourage students to write in their math journal about how they solved each problem.

Name_____   Date _____

Ink Drips

Directions

Fill in each ink drip with a number to make each equation correct.

1 $136 + \bigcirc = 141$

$\bigcirc =$ _____

2 $46 - 37 = \bigcirc$

$\bigcirc =$ _____

3 $49 - \bigcirc = 38$

$\bigcirc =$ _____

4 $4 + 4 - \bigcirc = 3$

$\bigcirc =$ _____

5 $3 + 6 + \bigcirc = 27$

$\bigcirc =$ _____

6 $4 + \bigcirc + 5 = 13$

$\bigcirc =$ _____

7 $36 + 6 - \bigcirc = 29$

$\bigcirc =$ _____

8 $121 - 64 + \bigcirc = 97$

$\bigcirc =$ _____

9 $\bigcirc + 16 - 3 = 41$

$\bigcirc =$ _____

10 $19 - 6 + \bigcirc = 26$

$\bigcirc =$ _____

Multilevel Math Fun • 3–5 © 2002 Creative Teaching Press

Name_____ Date_____

Ink Spots

Directions

Fill in each ink spot with a number to make each equation correct.

1 $(3,000 - 2,000) \times$ $= 1,000$

 = _____

7 $123 + 345 +$ $= 567$

 = _____

2 $- 6 + 3 = 18$

 = _____

8 $\frac{3}{5} \times \frac{5}{3} \times$ $= 2$

 = _____

3 $+ 99 + 9 = 1,107$

 = _____

9 $76 -$ $+ 13 = 15$

 = _____

4 $(666 - 555) \times$ $= 1,110$

 = _____

10 $(40 \times 40) - (39 \times$ $) = 1$

 = _____

5 $(\frac{1}{6} + \frac{1}{6}) \times \frac{2}{3} =$

 = _____

6 $31 -$ $+ 12 = 37$

 = _____

$5 \times 4 \times$ ⬤ $= 120$

Ink Stains

Directions

Fill in each ink stain with a number to make each equation correct.

1 $3{,}210 \div \bigcirc = 1{,}070$

$\bigcirc = $ _____

2 $2\frac{1}{2} + \bigcirc - 1 = 4\frac{5}{6}$

$\bigcirc = $ _____

3 $5 \times 6 \times 7 \times \bigcirc - 100 = 1{,}160$

$\bigcirc = $ _____

4 $\left(\frac{2}{3} \times \frac{5}{6}\right) + \bigcirc = 1$

$\bigcirc = $ _____

5 $\left(\frac{1}{8} + \frac{2}{8}\right) - \bigcirc = \frac{1}{8}$

$\bigcirc = $ _____

6 $9{,}999 - 7{,}881 - \bigcirc = 888$

$\bigcirc = $ _____

7 $3{,}996 \div \bigcirc = 666$

$\bigcirc = $ _____

8 $(3 \times 2 - 4) \times (12 - 6 \times \bigcirc) = 36$

$\bigcirc = $ _____

9 $\bigcirc + 13 - 41 + 14 = 17$

$\bigcirc = $ _____

10 $29 + \bigcirc + 29 - 92 = 58$

$\bigcirc = $ _____

Multilevel Math Fun • 3–5 © 2002 Creative Teaching Press

Name_____ Date_____

Ink Splotches

Directions

Fill in each ink splotch with a number to make each equation correct.

1 $0.85 + 4.5 + 0.14 + 2.5 + 81.0 + \bigcirc = 100.6$

$\bigcirc = $ _____

2 $(6 \times \bigcirc) - (8 \times \frac{1}{4}) = 2$

$\bigcirc = $ _____

3 $\frac{1}{4} + \frac{3}{8} + \frac{3}{4} + \bigcirc + \frac{1}{2} + \frac{3}{16} = 2\frac{1}{2}$

$\bigcirc = $ _____

4 $(4.5 \times 2.1 + \bigcirc) - (0.76 + 0.31 - 0.61) = 9.3$

$\bigcirc = $ _____

5 $(134 \times 195) - (56 \times \bigcirc) = 3{,}571 \times 6$

$\bigcirc = $ _____

6 $(656 \div \bigcirc) + (32 \times 26) = 106 \times 8$

$\bigcirc = $ _____

7 $(\bigcirc \times \frac{1}{3}) + (10 \times \frac{1}{2}) = 10$

$\bigcirc = $ _____

8 $1{,}341 \div 447 + \bigcirc - 52 = 612$

$\bigcirc = $ _____

9 $^-16 \times {^-32} + \bigcirc = {^-3}$

$\bigcirc = $ _____

10 $^-321 + 68 + \bigcirc = {^-300}$

$\bigcirc = $ _____

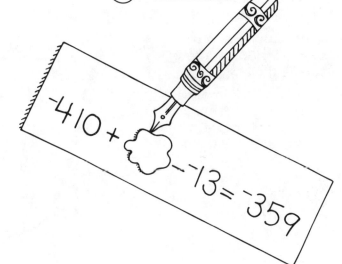

$^-410 + \bigcirc - {^-13} = {^-359}$

Input/Output

Levels

✔ **reproducibles (choose the appropriate level)**

1 ● Search for the Rule (page 43)
PROBLEM SOLVING AND ALGEBRA (ADDITION AND MULTIPLICATION)

2 ● Make a Rule (page 44)
PROBLEM SOLVING AND ALGEBRA (ADDITION, SUBTRACTION, AND MULTIPLICATION)

3 ● Write the Rule (page 45)
PROBLEM SOLVING AND ALGEBRA (ADDITION, SUBTRACTION, MULTIPLICATION, AND EXPONENTS)

4 ● Find a Rule (page 46)
PROBLEM SOLVING AND ALGEBRA (ADDITION, SUBTRACTION, MULTIPLICATION, EXPONENTS, AND DIVISION)

Directions

1 Give each student a reproducible at the appropriate level.

2 Tell students to look at the input and output numbers to figure out what rule was used to change the input numbers to the output numbers. Encourage them to only concentrate on one problem at a time.

3 Have students write the rule symbolically using ■ for input and ▲ for output. Explain to students that the rule to get from input to output must be written as an equation with at least one operation and an equals sign (e.g., ■ x 2 + 1 = ▲).

Helpful Hints

➤ Use the sample problem on each reproducible to show students how to complete the reproducibles.

➤ Invite students to use a calculator to help them find a rule for each problem.

➤ Make an overhead transparency of a reproducible. Divide the class into six teams, and have each team work together to solve one of the problems.

Name_____ Date _____

Search for the Rule

Look at each set of input and output numbers to figure out what rule was used to change the input numbers to the output numbers. (Concentrate on one problem at a time.) Write the rule symbolically using ■ for input and ▲ for output. The rule to get from input to output must be written as an equation with at least one operation and an equals sign (see sample problem).

Sample Problem

■ Input	▲ Output
0	0
8	8
6	6
2	?2
7	?7
3	?3

Rule: ■ + 0 = ▲
or ■ x 1 = ▲

①

■ Input	▲ Output
2	6
4	12
6	18
5	?
8	?
7	?

Rule:

②

■ Input	▲ Output
1	4
3	6
5	8
2	?
4	?
6	?

Rule:

③

■ Input	▲ Output
0	0
1	0
2	0
3	?
4	?
5	?

Rule:

④

■ Input	▲ Output
1	2
2	4
3	6
4	?
5	?
6	?

Rule:

⑤

■ Input	▲ Output
4	16
2	8
6	24
9	?
8	?
5	?

Rule:

Multilevel Math Fun • 3–5 © 2002 Creative Teaching Press

Make a Rule

Directions

Look at each set of input and output numbers to figure out what rule was used to change the input numbers to the output numbers. (Concentrate on one problem at a time.) Write the rule symbolically using ■ for input and ▲ for output. The rule to get from input to output must be written as an equation with at least one operation and an equals sign (see sample problem).

Sample Problem

■	▲
Input	Output
6	38
4	26
1	8
7	?44
2	?14
3	?20

Rule: ■ × 6 + 2 = ▲

①

■	▲
Input	Output
1	9
2	11
3	13
0	?
4	?
9	?

Rule:

②

■	▲
Input	Output
1	9
2	12
3	15
0	?
4	?
7	?

Rule:

③

■	▲
Input	Output
6	16
5	14
4	12
3	?
2	?
1	?

Rule:

④

■	▲
Input	Output
1	3
3	7
2	5
5	?
6	?
0	?

Rule:

⑤

■	▲
Input	Output
5	17
2	5
7	25
4	?
9	?
1	?

Rule:

Multilevel Math Fun • 3–5 © 2002 Creative Teaching Press

Write the Rule

Directions

Look at each set of input and output numbers to figure out what rule was used to change the input numbers to the output numbers. (Concentrate on one problem at a time.) Write the rule symbolically using ■ for input and ▲ for output. The rule to get from input to output must be written as an equation with at least one operation and an equals sign (see sample problem).

Sample Problem

■ Input	▲ Output
1	1
3	27
5	125
7	?343
9	?729
10	?1,000

Rule: $■^3 = ▲$
or ■ x ■ x ■ = ▲

①

■ Input	▲ Output
2	7
4	19
6	39
8	?
10	?
3	?

Rule:

②

■ Input	▲ Output
2	16
3	81
4	256
5	?
6	?
7	?

Rule:

③

■ Input	▲ Output
1	0
3	8
4	15
6	?
9	?
7	?

Rule:

④

■ Input	▲ Output
0	1
2	9
3	28
4	?
6	?
8	?

Rule:

⑤

■ Input	▲ Output
1	4
2	16
3	36
4	?
5	?
6	?

Rule:

Find a Rule

Directions

Look at each set of input and output numbers to figure out what rule was used to change the input numbers to the output numbers. (Concentrate on one problem at a time.) Write the rule symbolically using ■ for input and ▲ for output. The rule to get from input to output must be written as an equation with at least one operation and an equals sign (see sample problem).

Sample Problem

■ Input	▲ Output
2	6
4	20
5	30
6	?42
7	?56
1	?2

Rule: ■ x ■ + ■ = ▲

1

■ Input	▲ Output
2	2
8	5
6	4
4	?
0	?
10	?

Rule:

2

■ Input	▲ Output
2	7
3	26
0	⁻1
4	?
5	?
6	?

Rule:

3

■ Input	▲ Output
7	3
5	2
3	1
9	?
1	?
11	?

Rule:

4

■ Input	▲ Output
12	4
8	3
4	2
16	?
20	?
0	?

Rule:

5

■ Input	▲ Output
1	3
2	8
3	15
5	?
7	?
10	?

Rule:

Multilevel Math Fun • 3–5 © 2002 Creative Teaching Press

Spin Big!

Materials

Levels

✔ **reproducibles (choose the appropriate level)**

1. ● **Spin 50** (page 48)
   ADDITION OF 2 NUMBERS
2. ● **Spin 75** (page 49)
   ADDITION OF 3 NUMBERS
3. ● **Spin 100** (page 50)
   ADDITION, SUBTRACTION, MULTIPLICATION, OR DIVISION OF 2 NUMBERS
4. ● **Spin 200** (page 51)
   COMBINATION OF ADDITION, SUBTRACTION, MULTIPLICATION, AND DIVISION OF 3 NUMBERS

✔ **Spinner A** (page 87)

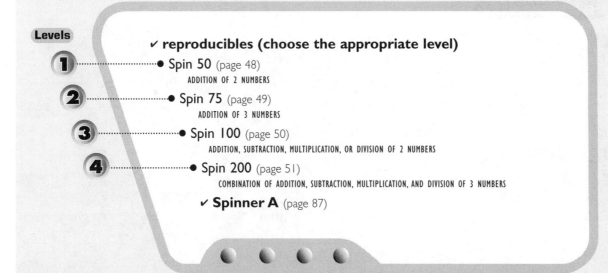

Directions

1 Give each pair of students a reproducible at the appropriate level and a spinner.

2 Tell students that the object of the game is to get as close to the target number as they can. Have players, in turn, spin and write the numbers in the boxes. For Spin 100 and Spin 200, tell players to decide which operation symbol(s) they wish to use on that turn and write them in the ovals. Have players write the answer to their equation in the last box.

3 Have players, on their first turn, write the answer to their equation on the line below "Accumulated Total." On all other turns, have players add their previous accumulated total to the answer to their equation and write their new total on the line. Tell players that they may reject any three spins, write the number at the bottom of their paper, and spin again during their turn.

4 Players do not have to have an accumulated total that equals the exact target number. They may exceed the target number or have a total less than it. A player may stop spinning at any time, but he or she may not exceed 10 turns. Once a player decides to stop, the accumulated total is his or her final score.

Helpful Hints

➤ Invite two teams of students to play instead of only two students.

➤ Add variety to the game by inviting students to choose which spinner they use for their game. (Spinner B on page 87 has numbers 0–9, Spinner C on page 88 has numbers 1–10, and Spinner D on page 88 has fractions ¼, ⅔, ½, ¾, ⅚, and ⅘.)

Names_____ Date _____

Spin 50

Directions

- The object of the game is to get as close to 50 as you can.

- Take turns. Spin the spinner twice, write the numbers in the boxes, write the sum of the numbers in the last box, and calculate your accumulated total. (You may reject any three spins, write the number at the bottom of the paper, and spin again during your turn.)

- Your total may be more than or less than 50. You may stop spinning at any time. Once you decide to stop, your accumulated total is your final score. The player whose final score is closest to 50 is the winner.

Player 1		**Player 2**	
Numbers Spun	**Accumulated Total**	**Numbers Spun**	**Accumulated Total**
☐ + ☐ = ☐	_____	☐ + ☐ = ☐	_____
☐ + ☐ = ☐	_____	☐ + ☐ = ☐	_____
☐ + ☐ = ☐	_____	☐ + ☐ = ☐	_____
☐ + ☐ = ☐	_____	☐ + ☐ = ☐	_____
☐ + ☐ = ☐	_____	☐ + ☐ = ☐	_____
☐ + ☐ = ☐	_____	☐ + ☐ = ☐	_____
☐ + ☐ = ☐	_____	☐ + ☐ = ☐	_____
☐ + ☐ = ☐	_____	☐ + ☐ = ☐	_____
☐ + ☐ = ☐	_____	☐ + ☐ = ☐	_____
☐ + ☐ = ☐	_____	☐ + ☐ = ☐	_____

Reject   **Reject**

☐ ☐ ☐   ☐ ☐ ☐

Multilevel Math Fun • 3–5 © 2002 Creative Teaching Press

Names_____ Date _____

Spin 75

Directions

- The object of the game is to get as close to 75 as you can.

- Take turns. Spin the spinner three times, write the numbers in the boxes, write the sum of the numbers in the last box, and calculate your accumulated total. (You may reject any three spins, write the number at the bottom of the paper, and spin again during your turn.)

- Your total may be more than or less than 75. You may stop spinning at any time. Once you decide to stop, your accumulated total is your final score. The player whose final score is closest to 75 is the winner.

Player 1	Player 2
Numbers Spun　　　**Accumulated Total**	**Numbers Spun**　　　**Accumulated Total**

Player 1

☐ + ☐ + ☐ = ☐ ____

☐ + ☐ + ☐ = ☐ ____

☐ + ☐ + ☐ = ☐ ____

☐ + ☐ + ☐ = ☐ ____

☐ + ☐ + ☐ = ☐ ____

☐ + ☐ + ☐ = ☐ ____

☐ + ☐ + ☐ = ☐ ____

☐ + ☐ + ☐ = ☐ ____

☐ + ☐ + ☐ = ☐ ____

☐ + ☐ + ☐ = ☐ ____

Reject

☐　☐　☐

Player 2

☐ + ☐ + ☐ = ☐ ____

☐ + ☐ + ☐ = ☐ ____

☐ + ☐ + ☐ = ☐ ____

☐ + ☐ + ☐ = ☐ ____

☐ + ☐ + ☐ = ☐ ____

☐ + ☐ + ☐ = ☐ ____

☐ + ☐ + ☐ = ☐ ____

☐ + ☐ + ☐ = ☐ ____

☐ + ☐ + ☐ = ☐ ____

☐ + ☐ + ☐ = ☐ ____

Reject

☐　☐　☐

Spin 100

Directions

- The object of the game is to get as close to 100 as you can.

- Take turns. Spin the spinner twice and write the numbers in the boxes. Decide which operation symbol (+, −, x, ÷) you wish to use on that turn and write it in the oval. Write the answer to the equation and calculate your accumulated total. (You may reject any three spins, write the number at the bottom of the paper, and spin again during your turn.)

- Your total may be more than or less than 100. You may stop spinning at any time. Once you decide to stop, your accumulated total is your final score. The player whose final score is closest to 100 is the winner.

	Player I				Player I		
Numbers Spun			**Accumulated Total**	**Numbers Spun**			**Accumulated Total**
☐	◯	☐ = ☐	___	☐	◯	☐ = ☐	___
☐	◯	☐ = ☐	___	☐	◯	☐ = ☐	___
☐	◯	☐ = ☐	___	☐	◯	☐ = ☐	___
☐	◯	☐ = ☐	___	☐	◯	☐ = ☐	___
☐	◯	☐ = ☐	___	☐	◯	☐ = ☐	___
☐	◯	☐ = ☐	___	☐	◯	☐ = ☐	___
☐	◯	☐ = ☐	___	☐	◯	☐ = ☐	___
☐	◯	☐ = ☐	___	☐	◯	☐ = ☐	___
☐	◯	☐ = ☐	___	☐	◯	☐ = ☐	___
☐	◯	☐ = ☐	___	☐	◯	☐ = ☐	___

Reject

☐ ☐ ☐   ☐ ☐ ☐

Multilevel Math Fun • 3–5 © 2002 Creative Teaching Press

Spin 200

Directions

- The object of the game is to get as close to 200 as you can.

- Take turns. Spin the spinner three times and write the numbers in the boxes. Decide which operation symbols (+, −, x, ÷) you wish to use on that turn and write them in the ovals. (For each equation, you may use the same operation in both ovals or a combination of two different ones.) Write the answer to the equation and calculate your accumulated total. (You may reject any three spins, write the number at the bottom of the paper, and spin again during your turn.)

- Your total may be more than or less than 200. You may stop spinning at any time. Once you decide to stop, your accumulated total is your final score. The player whose final score is closest to 200 is the winner.

Player 1		Player 2	
Numbers Spun	Accumulated Total	Numbers Spun	Accumulated Total

Reject

Smallest Answer Path

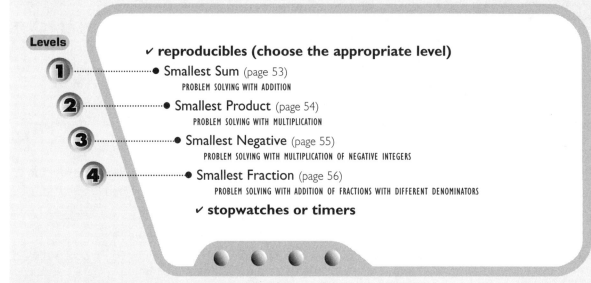

Levels

✔ **reproducibles (choose the appropriate level)**

1 ● Smallest Sum (page 53)
PROBLEM SOLVING WITH ADDITION

2 ● Smallest Product (page 54)
PROBLEM SOLVING WITH MULTIPLICATION

3 ● Smallest Negative (page 55)
PROBLEM SOLVING WITH MULTIPLICATION OF NEGATIVE INTEGERS

4 ● Smallest Fraction (page 56)
PROBLEM SOLVING WITH ADDITION OF FRACTIONS WITH DIFFERENT DENOMINATORS

✔ **stopwatches or timers**

« Directions

1 Give each pair of students two copies of the same reproducible at the appropriate level and a stopwatch or timer.

2 Tell students that the object of the game is to find the path of less than 10 numbers with the smallest sum or product (depending on the reproducible) in the least amount of time. (Note: Students can only move horizontally and vertically, not diagonally.)

3 Set a time limit for the game, or have students continue to play until each player completes his or her path.

4 Invite students to begin their path in the top row and end it in the bottom row. Have them connect the squares of numbers by drawing a line or lightly shading the boxes.

5 Tell players to record the time it took them to complete their paper and the sum or product of their number path. Then, have them compare their answers with their partner's paper to see who found the smallest sum or product in the least amount of time.

Helpful Hints

➤ Remind students working on the Smallest Fraction reproducible that the larger the denominator, the smaller the fraction (e.g., $1/16$ is smaller than $1/8$).

➤ Remind students working on the Smallest Negative reproducible that the smallest sum is the largest negative number (e.g., -6 is smaller than -3) and that two negatives multiplied together equal a positive number.

Name_____   Date _____

Smallest Sum

Directions

- The object of the game is to find the path of **8** numbers with the smallest sum in the least amount of time. (Note: Only move horizontally and vertically, not diagonally.)

- Begin your path in the top row and end it in the bottom row. Connect squares of numbers by drawing a line or lightly shading the boxes.

- Record the time it took you to finish your path and the sum of your path. Compare your sum with your partner's sum to see who found the smallest sum in the least amount of time.

Add to find the smallest sum.

10	8	12	9	17
14	27	53	20	42
8	20	40	45	85
16	8	14	3	40
49	82	17	2	10

I finished my path in _____.

My sum is _____. My partner's sum is _____.

Name_____ Date _____

Smallest Product

Directions

- The object of the game is to find the path of **6** numbers with the smallest product in the least amount of time. (Note: Only move horizontally and vertically, not diagonally.)

- Begin your path in the top row and end it in the bottom row. Connect squares of numbers by drawing a line or lightly shading the boxes.

- Record the time it took you to finish your path and the product of your path. Compare your product with your partner's product to see who found the smallest product in the least amount of time.

Find the path to the smallest product.

2	7	8	6	4	8
9	1	9	4	3	9
3	8	4	2	5	7
5	2	7	1	3	3
7	6	4	4	6	1

I finished my path in _____.

My product is _____. My partner's product is _____.

Multilevel Math Fun • 3–5 © 2002 Creative Teaching Press

Name_____ Date _____

Smallest Negative

Multilevel Math Fun • 3–5 © 2002 Creative Teaching Press

Directions

Multiply to find the smallest negative product.

- The object of the game is to find the path of **9** negative numbers with the smallest negative product in the least amount of time. (Note: Only move horizontally and vertically, not diagonally.)

- Begin your path in the top row and end it in the bottom row. Connect squares of negative numbers by drawing a line or lightly shading the boxes.

- Record the time it took you to finish your path and the product of your path. Compare your product with your partner's product to see who found the smallest negative product in the least amount of time.

⁻1	⁻3	⁻6	⁻5	⁻4	⁻2
⁻8	⁻1	⁻2	⁻7	⁻3	⁻9
⁻7	⁻8	⁻4	⁻2	⁻4	⁻8
⁻9	⁻3	⁻5	⁻1	⁻9	⁻5
⁻4	⁻1	⁻2	⁻2	⁻6	⁻1

I finished my path in _____.

My negative product is _____. My partner's negative product is _____.

Name_____ Date _____

Smallest Fraction

Find the path that adds up to the smallest fraction.

Directions

- The object of the game is to find the path of **5** fractions with the smallest sum in the least amount of time. (Note: Only move horizontally and vertically, not diagonally.)

- Begin your path in the top row and end it in the bottom row. Connect the squares of fractions by drawing a line or lightly shading the boxes.

- Record the time it took you to finish your path and the sum of your path. Compare your sum with your partner's sum to see who found the smallest sum in the least amount of time.

$\frac{1}{2}$	$\frac{1}{4}$	$\frac{1}{3}$	$\frac{4}{6}$	$\frac{2}{3}$
$\frac{4}{6}$	$\frac{3}{4}$	$\frac{2}{4}$	$\frac{1}{3}$	$\frac{2}{6}$
$\frac{1}{3}$	$\frac{5}{6}$	$\frac{2}{3}$	$\frac{1}{4}$	$\frac{1}{2}$
$\frac{2}{4}$	1	$\frac{1}{3}$	$\frac{2}{6}$	2
$\frac{1}{2}$	$\frac{3}{4}$	$\frac{2}{3}$	$\frac{1}{6}$	$\frac{3}{4}$

I finished my path in _____.

My sum is _____. My partner's sum is _____.

Multilevel Math Fun • 3–5 © 2002 Creative Teaching Press

Frame It

Materials

Levels

✔ **reproducibles (choose the appropriate level)**

1 ● Baseball Frame (page 58)
ADDITION; MULTIPLICATION; SUBTRACTION OF DECIMALS

2 ● Basketball Frame (page 59)
ADDITION, SUBTRACTION, AND MULTIPLICATION OF FRACTIONS; DIVISION

3 ● Tennis Frame (page 60)
ADDITION, MULTIPLICATION, AND DIVISION OF WHOLE NUMBERS, FRACTIONS, AND DECIMALS

4 ● Golf Frame (page 61)
MULTIPLICATION OF FRACTIONS; DIVISION OF WHOLE NUMBERS, FRACTIONS, AND DECIMALS; PERCENTS

✔ **Spinner B** (page 87)

✔ **calculators (optional)**

Directions

Helpful Hints

➤ This game requires critical thinking and problem-solving skills. Encourage students to carefully look at their paper and at each math problem and place numbers in circles accordingly.

➤ Have students begin by playing each game on their paper separately. When they are comfortable with the rules, encourage them to play several or all four games at the same time. (Students will have more choice of where they can place their numbers, which requires more problem-solving skills.)

1 Give each pair of students a reproducible at the appropriate level and a spinner.

2 Choose a rule or have players choose a rule for each of the four games on their paper and record it in the appropriate place. For example, the rule might be that the winner is the player with the largest answer or the player with the smallest answer. (Students can use the same rule for each game or a different rule for each game.)

3 Have players, in turn, spin and write the number in any circle. (Once a number is placed, it cannot be moved.)

4 After players have written numbers in all the circles, have them complete the problem.

5 Have players look at the rule they recorded for the completed game, determine a winner, and record 1 point next to "Player 1" or "Player 2" at the top of the game board. The player with the most points after playing all four games is the winner. If there is a tie, encourage players to replay one of the games or create their own game on the back of their paper.

Names_____ Date _____

Baseball Frame

Directions

- Choose a rule (e.g., largest answer, smallest answer, answer closest to 100) for each game and record it on your paper. You can use the same rule for each game or a different one for each game.

- Take turns. Spin the spinner and write the number in any circle. (Once a number is placed, it cannot be moved.)

- Write numbers in all the circles. Then, complete the problem and record the answer on your paper.

- Look at the rule you recorded for the completed game. Determine a winner. Record 1 point next to "Player 1" or "Player 2" at the top of the game board. The player with the most points after playing all four games is the winner. If there is a tie, replay one of the games or create your own game on the back of the paper.

	Player 1	**Player 2**
Game 1 Rule:	+ ○ ○ ○ ○ ○ ○	+ ○ ○ ○ ○ ○ ○
Game 2 Rule:	○ ○ × ○	○ ○ × ○
Game 3 Rule:	○ × ○ + ○ + ○ =	○ × ○ + ○ + ○ =
Game 4 Rule:	○ . ○ ○ − ○ . ○ ○	○ . ○ ○ − ○ . ○ ○

Multilevel Math Fun • 3–5 © 2002 Creative Teaching Press

Names_____ Date _____

 # Basketball Frame

Directions

- Choose a rule (e.g., largest answer, smallest answer, answer closest to 100) for each game and record it on your paper. You can use the same rule for each game or a different one for each game.

- Take turns. Spin the spinner and write the number in any circle. (Once a number is placed, it cannot be moved.)

- Write numbers in all the circles. Then, complete the problem and record the answer on your paper.

- Look at the rule you recorded for the completed game. Determine a winner. Record 1 point next to "Player 1" or "Player 2" at the top of the game board. The player with the most points after playing all four games is the winner. If there is a tie, replay one of the games or create your own game on the back of the paper.

	Player 1	**Player 2**
Game 1 Rule:	___ + ___ + ___ =	___ + ___ + ___ =
Game 2 Rule:	___ x ___ =	___ x ___ =
Game 3 Rule:	___)‾‾‾	___)‾‾‾
Game 4 Rule:	___ x ___ − ___ =	___ x ___ − ___ =

Multilevel Math Fun • 3–5 © 2002 Creative Teaching Press

Names_____ Date _____

Tennis Frame

Directions

- Choose a rule (e.g., largest answer, smallest answer, answer closest to 100) for each game and record it on your paper. You can use the same rule for each game or a different one for each game.

- Take turns. Spin the spinner and write the number in any circle. (Once a number is placed, it cannot be moved.)

- Write numbers in all the circles. Then, complete the problem and record the answer on your paper.

- Look at the rule you recorded for the completed game. Determine a winner. Record 1 point next to "Player 1" or "Player 2" at the top of the game board. The player with the most points after playing all four games is the winner. If there is a tie, replay one of the games or create your own game on the back of the paper.

	Player 1	**Player 2**
Game 1 **Rule:**	⊘ x ⊘/⊘ + ⊘ =	⊘ x ⊘/⊘ + ⊘ =
Game 2 **Rule:**	⊘/⊘ ÷ ⊘/⊘ =	⊘/⊘ ÷ ⊘/⊘ =
Game 3 **Rule:**	⊘⊘⟌⊘⊘	⊘⊘⟌⊘⊘
Game 4 **Rule:**	⊘⊘⊘. x ⊘⊘.⊘ ____	⊘⊘⊘. x ⊘⊘.⊘ ____

Multilevel Math Fun • 3–5 © 2002 Creative Teaching Press

Names_____ Date _____

Golf Frame

Directions

- Choose a rule (e.g., largest answer, smallest answer, answer closest to 100) for each game and record it on your paper. You can use the same rule for each game or a different one for each game.

- Take turns. Spin the spinner and write the number in any circle. (Once a number is placed, it cannot be moved.)

- Write numbers in all the circles. Then, complete the problem and record the answer on your paper.

- Look at the rule you recorded for the completed game. Determine a winner. Record 1 point next to "Player 1" or "Player 2" at the top of the game board. The player with the most points after playing all four games is the winner. If there is a tie, replay one of the games or create your own game on the back of the paper.

	Player 1	**Player 2**
Game 1 Rule:	◯◯ % of ◯ =	◯◯ % of ◯ =
Game 2 Rule:	.◯◯ ◯)◯◯◯	.◯◯ ◯)◯◯◯
Game 3 Rule:	◯◯◯)◯◯◯	◯◯◯)◯◯◯
Game 4 Rule:	◯/◯ × ◯/◯ ÷ ◯/◯ =	◯/◯ × ◯/◯ ÷ ◯/◯ =

Factor It

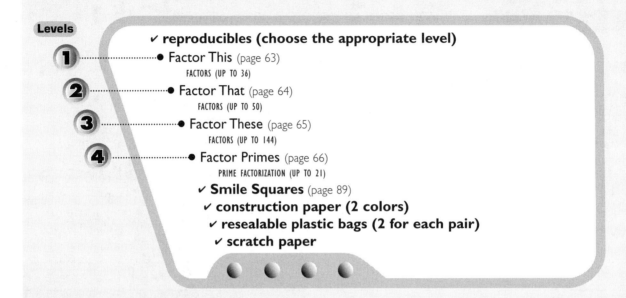

Levels

✔ reproducibles (choose the appropriate level)

① ● Factor This (page 63)
FACTORS (UP TO 36)

② ● Factor That (page 64)
FACTORS (UP TO 50)

③ ● Factor These (page 65)
FACTORS (UP TO 144)

④ ● Factor Primes (page 66)
PRIME FACTORIZATION (UP TO 21)

✔ Smile Squares (page 89)
✔ construction paper (2 colors)
✔ resealable plastic bags (2 for each pair)
✔ scratch paper

Directions

Helpful Hints

➤ Review factors, prime numbers, and prime factorization with the whole class prior to having students play this game. (Students can limit the points their partner can earn by choosing a prime number.)

➤ Have players check each other's factors before awarding points.

➤ Encourage players to keep track of their scores on a small white board or chalkboard or on a piece of paper.

1 Photocopy on two colors of construction paper a set of Smile Squares for each pair. Cut apart the Smile Squares, and store each color set in a separate bag.

2 Give each pair of students a reproducible at the appropriate level, scratch paper, and two bags of Smile Squares (two different colors).

3 Tell player 1 to choose a number on the game board, and cover it with a Smile Square. Tell player 1 to record this number as the number of points he or she receives for this round.

4 Tell player 2 to write on scratch paper all the factors for the number chosen by player 1. Then, have him or her cover the available numbers on the game board with Smile Squares (different color from player 1). (Players can only cover a number once. When a number is covered, it cannot be used in another round to score points.) Have player 2 add together the numbers he or she covered on this turn and record the sum as his or her points for this round.

5 Have players alternate roles until all the squares on the game board are covered.

Factor This

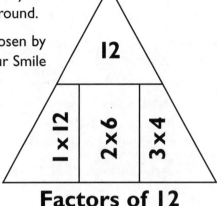

Factors of 12

The triangle shows: 12 at top; bottom row: 1 x 12, 2 x 6, 3 x 4

Directions

- <u>Player 1</u>: Choose a number on the game board. Cover it with one of your Smile Squares. Record this as the number of points you receive for this round.

- <u>Player 2</u>: Write on scratch paper all the factors for the number chosen by player 1. Cover the available numbers on the game board with your Smile Squares. (You can only cover a number once. When a number is covered, it cannot be used in another round to score points.) Add together the numbers you covered on this turn. Record the sum as the number of points you receive for this round.

- Take turns being player 1. Continue to play until all the squares on the game board are covered. The player with the greatest number of points is the winner.

1	2	3	4	5	6
7	8	9	10	11	12
13	14	15	16	17	18
19	20	21	22	23	24
25	26	27	28	29	30
31	32	33	34	35	36

Factor That

Directions

- <u>Player 1</u>: Choose a number on the game board. Cover it with one of your Smile Squares. Record this as the number of points you receive for this round.

- <u>Player 2</u>: Write on scratch paper all the factors for the number chosen by player 1. Cover the available numbers on the game board with your Smile Squares. (You can only cover a number once. When a number is covered, it cannot be used in another round to score points.) Add together the numbers you covered on this turn. Record the sum as the number of points you receive for this round.

- Take turns being player 1. Continue to play until all the squares on the game board are covered. The player with the greatest number of points is the winner.

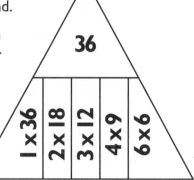

Factors of 36

1	2	3	4	5
6	7	8	9	10
11	12	13	14	15
16	17	18	19	20
21	22	23	24	25
26	27	28	29	30
31	32	33	34	35
36	37	38	39	40
41	42	43	44	45
46	47	48	49	50

Multilevel Math Fun • 3–5 © 2002 Creative Teaching Press

Factor These

Directions

- <u>Player 1</u>: Choose a number on the game board. Cover it with one of your Smile Squares. Record this as the number of points you receive for this round.

- <u>Player 2</u>: Write on scratch paper all the factors for the number chosen by player 1. Cover the available numbers on the game board with your Smile Squares. (You can only cover a number once. When a number is covered, it cannot be used in another round to score points.) Add together the numbers you covered on this turn. Record the sum as the number of points you receive for this round.

- Take turns being player 1. Continue to play until all the squares on the game board are covered. The player with the greatest number of points is the winner.

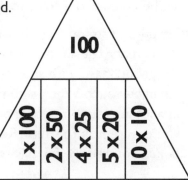

Factors of 100

1	22	54	11	35	63
12	48	120	88	10	40
33	121	2	49	20	90
56	60	18	110	30	64
42	100	84	3	77	80
16	4	81	45	36	8
32	9	21	50	132	44
99	28	70	5	144	96
6	72	25	108	15	27
24	1	55	14	66	7

Factor Primes

Prime Factors
of 18 = 2, 3, 3

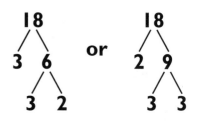

2	1	18	2	10	2
1	2	3	17	2	3
3	2	1	2	13	3
2	5	14	2	6	1
2	8	3	1	7	2
11	2	16	2	1	7
19	2	1	12	5	3
4	19	3	2	11	2
1	2	5	15	7	2
13	20	2	7	5	9
3	5	3	17	3	21

Multilevel Math Fun • 3–5 © 2002 Creative Teaching Press

Close to the Target

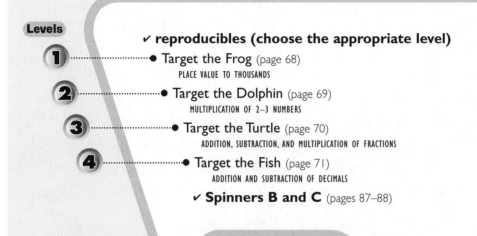

Materials

Levels

✔ **reproducibles (choose the appropriate level)**

1 ● Target the Frog (page 68)
   PLACE VALUE TO THOUSANDS

2 ● Target the Dolphin (page 69)
   MULTIPLICATION OF 2–3 NUMBERS

3 ● Target the Turtle (page 70)
   ADDITION, SUBTRACTION, AND MULTIPLICATION OF FRACTIONS

4 ● Target the Fish (page 71)
   ADDITION AND SUBTRACTION OF DECIMALS

✔ **Spinners B and C** (pages 87–88)

Directions

Helpful Hints

➣ This game requires problem-solving skills. Encourage students to carefully look at each math problem and place numbers in spaces and reject numbers based on what numbers will help them get closest to their target number.

➣ Invite players to use a calculator to check each other's work.

1 Divide the class into small groups. Give each student in a group the same reproducible at the appropriate level, and give each group the appropriate spinner.

2 Tell students that the object of the game is to write numbers in the spaces so each answer is as close to its target answer as students can get.

3 Have players, in turn, spin and write the number in any space until all the spaces are filled. (Players cannot move the number to a different space once it has been written and can only fill in one space on each turn.)

4 Ask players to solve each problem on their paper to determine how close each answer is to its target answer. Have them subtract to find the difference between the target answer and their answer, and then record the difference. (Their answer may be under or over the target answer. It only matters how close the answer is.)

5 Tell players to add their differences together to find their "total difference." The winner is the player with the smallest total difference (i.e., the player with the closest answers to the target answers).

Name_____   Date _____

Target the Frog

Directions

- The object of the game is to write digits in the ovals so each answer (number) is as close to its target number as you can get.

- Spin **Spinner B.** Write the digit in any oval. Take turns until all the ovals are filled.

- Look at each section of your paper. Write the number made from the digits in the ovals in the appropriate column. Subtract to find the difference between the target number and your number. Record the difference. (Your number may be under or over the target number.)

- Add your differences together to find your "total difference." Record it on the line. The winner is the player with the smallest total difference.

Target Number	Your Digits	Your Answer (Number)	Your Difference
5	⬭		
20	⬭⬭		
300	⬭⬭⬭		
5,000	⬭,⬭⬭⬭		

Total Difference _____

Multilevel Math Fun • 3–5 © 2002 Creative Teaching Press

Name_____ Date _____

Target the Dolphin

Directions

- The object of the game is to write numbers in the ovals so each answer (product) is as close to the target answer as you can get.

- Spin **Spinner C.** Write the number in any oval. Take turns until all the ovals are filled.

- Multiply the numbers in each section of your paper. Write each product in the appropriate column. Subtract to find the difference between the target answer and your product. Record the difference. (Your product may be under or over the target answer.)

- Add your differences together to find your "total difference." Record it on the line. The winner is the player with the smallest total difference.

Target Answer	Your Numbers	Your Answer (Product)	Your Difference
10	◯ x ◯		
50	◯ x ◯		
100	◯ x ◯ x ◯		
500	◯ x ◯ x ◯		

Total Difference _____

Name_____   Date _____

Target the Turtle

Directions

- The object of the game is to write numbers in the circles so each answer (fraction) equals as close to its target answer as you can get.

- Spin **Spinner C.** Write the number in any circle. Take turns until all the circles are filled.

- Perform the operation shown in each section of your paper and write the calculated fraction. (The first answer is the fraction created. No operation is required.) Subtract to find the difference between the target answer and your fraction. Record the difference. (Your fraction may be under or over the target answer.)

- Add your differences together to find your "total difference." Record it on the line. The winner is the player with the smallest total difference.

Target Answer	Your Numbers	Your Answer (Fraction)	Your Difference
2	$\frac{\bigcirc}{\bigcirc}$		
1	$\frac{\bigcirc}{\bigcirc} + \frac{\bigcirc}{\bigcirc}$		
$\frac{1}{2}$	$\frac{\bigcirc}{\bigcirc} - \frac{\bigcirc}{\bigcirc}$		
$1\frac{1}{2}$	$\frac{\bigcirc}{\bigcirc} \times \frac{\bigcirc}{\bigcirc}$		

Total Difference _____

Multilevel Math Fun • 3–5 © 2002 Creative Teaching Press

Name_____ Date _____

Target the Fish

Directions

- The object of the game is to write numbers in the circles so each answer (decimal) is as close to its target answer as you can get.

- Spin **Spinner B.** Write the number in any circle. Take turns until all the circles are filled.

- Perform the operation shown in each section of your paper and write the calculated decimal. (In the first and second sections, the answer is the decimal created. No operation is required.) Subtract to find the difference between the target answer and your decimal. Record the difference. (Your decimal may be under or over the target answer.)

- Add your differences together to find your "total difference." Record it on the line. The winner is the player with the smallest total difference.

Target Answer	Your Numbers	Your Answer (Decimal)	Your Difference
1	◯.◯◯		
5	◯.◯◯◯		
10	◯◯.◯◯◯ + ◯.◯◯◯		
100	◯◯◯.◯◯ − ◯◯.◯◯		

Total Difference _____

Multilevel Math Fun • 3-5 © 2002 Creative Teaching Press

Speed Wheel

Materials

Levels

✔ **reproducibles (choose the appropriate level)**

1 ········● Number Speed (page 73)
ADDITION, SUBTRACTION, MULTIPLICATION, OR DIVISION OF WHOLE NUMBERS

2 ········● Decimal Speed (page 74)
ADDITION, SUBTRACTION, MULTIPLICATION, OR DIVISION OF DECIMALS

3 ········● Fraction Speed (page 75)
ADDITION, SUBTRACTION, MULTIPLICATION, OR DIVISION OF FRACTIONS

4 ········● Negative Speed (page 76)
ADDITION, SUBTRACTION, MULTIPLICATION, OR DIVISION OF ZERO AND NEGATIVE INTEGERS

✔ **stopwatches or timers**

✔ **calculators**

Directions

Helpful Hints

➤ Laminate the reproducibles, and have students write on them with dry erase markers. If you don't laminate game boards, each player will need five reproducibles.

➤ Invite students to race against themselves. Have them complete the reproducible several times with different numbers in the center and try to complete it quicker each time.

➤ Use correction fluid to delete the numbers in the speed wheel. Write new numbers in the spaces.

1 Divide the class into small groups. Give each student in a group the same reproducible at the appropriate level, and give each group a stopwatch or timer and a calculator.

2 Choose a number for players to write in the middle of their speed wheel and an operation to perform, or have players agree on a number and an operation. Have players record this information on their paper before they begin the game.

3 Set a time limit for the game, or have groups play until all players complete their speed wheel. Tell players to record the time it took them to complete the speed wheel.

4 Have players check their answers with a calculator and record how many correct answers they wrote. The player with the most correct answers in the least amount of time is the winner.

5 Encourage groups to play five games, each with a different number in the center circle or a different operation. The player who wins the most games is the overall winner.

Name_____ Date _____

Number Speed

Directions

- Choose a number to write in the middle of your speed wheel and an operation to perform. (All players in your group must play with the same number and operation.) Record this information on your paper before you begin the game.

- Set a time limit for the game, or play until all players complete their speed wheel. Record the time it took you to complete your speed wheel.

- Check your answers. Record how many correct answers you wrote. The player with the most correct answers in the least amount of time is the winner.

- Play five games. Change the center number or the operation for each game. The player who wins the most games is the overall winner.

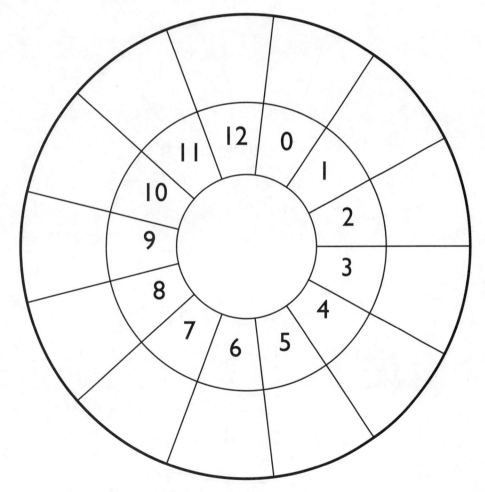

Operation: _____

Time to complete speed wheel: _____ Number of correct answers: _____

Decimal Speed

Directions

- Choose a number to write in the middle of your speed wheel and an operation to perform. (All players in your group must play with the same number and operation.) Record this information on your paper before you begin the game.

- Set a time limit for the game, or play until all players complete their speed wheel. Record the time it took you to complete your speed wheel.

- Check your answers. Record how many correct answers you wrote. The player with the most correct answers in the least amount of time is the winner.

- Play five games. Change the center number or the operation for each game. The player who wins the most games is the overall winner.

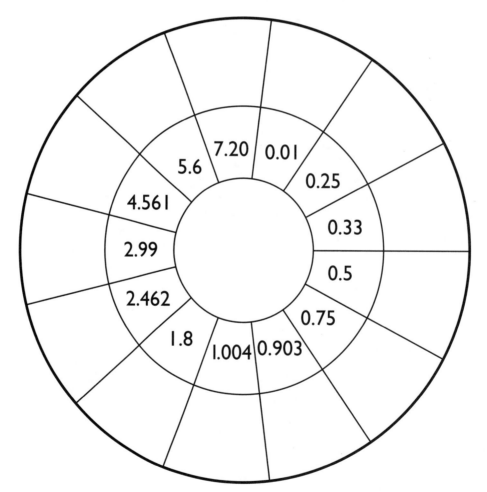

Operation: _____

Time to complete speed wheel: _____ Number of correct answers: _____

Multilevel Math Fun • 3–5 © 2002 Creative Teaching Press

Name_____ Date _____

Fraction Speed

Directions

- Choose a number to write in the middle of your speed wheel and an operation to perform. (All players in your group must play with the same number and operation.) Record this information on your paper before you begin the game.

- Set a time limit for the game, or play until all players complete their speed wheel. Record the time it took you to complete your speed wheel.

- Check your answers. Record how many correct answers you wrote. The player with the most correct answers in the least amount of time is the winner.

- Play five games. Change the center number or the operation for each game. The player who wins the most games is the overall winner.

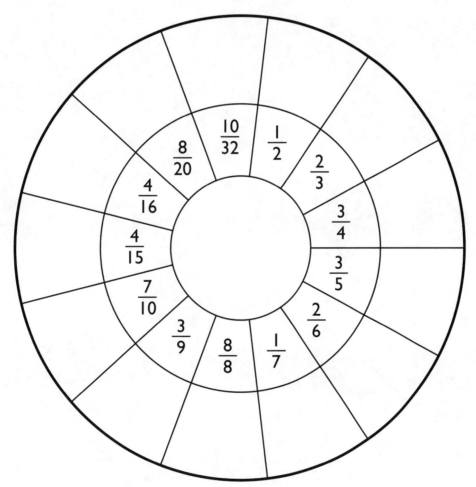

Operation: _____

Time to complete speed wheel: _____ Number of correct answers: _____

Negative Speed

Directions

- Choose a number to write in the middle of your speed wheel and an operation to perform. (All players in your group must play with the same number and operation.) Record this information on your paper before you begin the game.

- Set a time limit for the game, or play until all players complete their speed wheel. Record the time it took you to complete the speed wheel.

- Check your answers. Record how many correct answers you wrote. The player with the most correct answers in the least amount of time is the winner.

- Play five games. Change the center number or the operation for each game. The player who wins the most games is the overall winner.

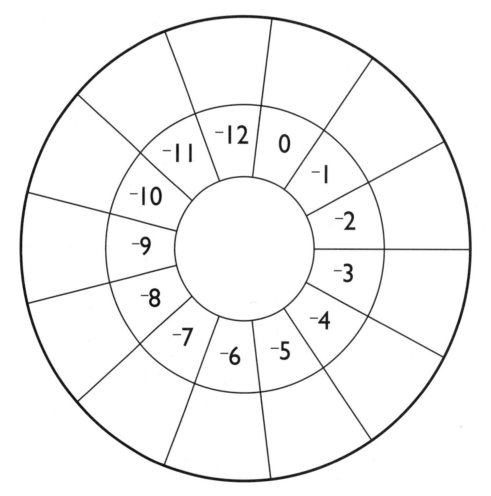

Operation: _____

Time to complete speed wheel: _____   Number of correct answers: _____

Multilevel Math Fun • 3–5 © 2002 Creative Teaching Press

Fractions in a Row

✔ **Fraction Rules Sheet** (page 78)
   FRACTIONS, IMPROPER FRACTIONS, MIXED NUMBERS, REDUCING FRACTIONS
✔ **Fraction Cards Set A** (page 90)
✔ **Fraction Cards Set B** (page 91)
✔ **Fraction Caller Cards** (page 92)
✔ **Airplane Fraction Board** (page 79)
✔ **construction paper**
✔ **large envelopes**
✔ **resealable plastic bags**

« Directions

Helpful Hints

➤ Photocopy Fraction Cards Set A and Set B on different colored construction paper so students can easily identify their cutouts.

➤ Photocopy the Fraction Caller Cards on white construction paper. Ask volunteers to help you lightly shade the cutouts with a colored pencil. Color each set a different color so they can be easily separated.

1 Photocopy on construction paper the Fraction Rules Sheet, both sets of fraction cards, the Fraction Caller Cards, and the Airplane Fraction Board. Cut apart the rules sheet and the fraction cards. Read the rules sheet to see what materials each game needs. Place a rules sheet, two Airplane Fraction Boards, and the appropriate set of fraction cards in a large envelope, and label it with the game's title. Cut apart the caller cards, place each set in a separate bag, label the bags *Caller Cards for (game title),* and place them in the appropriate envelope.

2 Divide the class into groups of two or three students. Give each group an envelope of game materials. Invite students to choose a "caller" for their game. (If three students are in a group, have them alternate playing and being the caller.)

3 Have each player place his or her fraction cards facedown in a pile. Have the caller place the caller cards facedown in a pile. Tell players to draw nine of their fraction cards and place them faceup on their game board.

4 Ask the caller to choose a caller card and read it aloud. If a player has that fraction card on his or her board, he or she removes it. Tell students to continue to play until a player removes three cards in a row horizontally, vertically, or diagonally.

Fraction Rules Sheet

Fractions, Fractions

- Play with two Airplane Fraction Boards, two sets of Fraction Cards Set A, and one set of Fraction Caller Cards Set A.
- Choose a "caller" for your game.
- <u>Players 1 and 2</u>: Place your Fraction Cards facedown in a pile. Draw nine of your Fraction Cards and place them faceup on your game board.
- <u>Caller</u>: Place the Fraction Caller Cards facedown in a pile. Choose one Fraction Caller Card at a time and read it aloud.
- <u>Players 1 and 2</u>: If you have the Fraction Card on your board, remove it. Play until a player removes three cards in a row horizontally, vertically, or diagonally. Play until a player wins five games.

Improper Fractions

- Play with two Airplane Fraction Boards, two sets of Fraction Cards Set B, and one set of Fraction Caller Cards Set B.
- Choose a "caller" for your game.
- <u>Players 1 and 2</u>: Place your Fraction Cards facedown in a pile. Draw nine of your Fraction Cards and place them faceup on your game board.
- <u>Caller</u>: Place the Fraction Caller Cards facedown in a pile. Choose one Fraction Caller Card at a time and read it aloud.
- <u>Players 1 and 2</u>: If you have the Fraction Card on your board, remove it. (You will need to read your fraction as an improper fraction.) Play until a player removes three cards in a row horizontally, vertically, or diagonally. Play until a player wins five games.

Mixed Number Fractions

- Play with two Airplane Fraction Boards, two sets of Fraction Cards Set B, and one set of Fraction Caller Cards Set C.
- Choose a "caller" for your game.
- <u>Players 1 and 2</u>: Place your Fraction Cards facedown in a pile. Draw nine of your Fraction Cards and place them faceup on your game board.
- <u>Caller</u>: Place the Fraction Caller Cards facedown in a pile. Choose one Fraction Caller Card at a time and read it aloud.
- <u>Players 1 and 2</u>: If you have the Fraction Card on your board, remove it. (You will need to read your fraction as a mixed number.) Play until a player removes three cards in a row horizontally, vertically, or diagonally. Play until a player wins five games.

Reduce the Fractions

- Play with two Airplane Fraction Boards, two sets of Fraction Cards Set A, and one set of Fraction Caller Cards Set D.
- Choose a "caller" for your game.
- <u>Players 1 and 2</u>: Place your Fraction Cards facedown in a pile. Draw nine of your Fraction Cards and place them faceup on your game board.
- <u>Caller</u>: Place the Fraction Caller Cards facedown in a pile. Choose one Fraction Caller Card at a time and read it aloud.
- <u>Players 1 and 2</u>: If you have the Fraction Card on your board, remove it. (You will need to reduce the fraction.) Play until a player removes three cards in a row horizontally, vertically, or diagonally. Play until a player wins five games.

Multilevel Math Fun • 3–5 © 2002 Creative Teaching Press

Airplane Fraction Board

Score More

Levels

✔ **reproducibles (choose the appropriate level)**

1 ⋯⋯ ● Square Score (page 81)
ADDITION OR SUBTRACTION OF TWO NUMBERS (4–9)

2 ⋯⋯ ● Circle Score (page 82)
ADDITION, SUBTRACTION, OR MULTIPLICATION OF TWO NUMBERS (0–9)

3 ⋯⋯ ● Hexagon Score (page 83)
ADDITION, SUBTRACTION, MULTIPLICATION, OR DIVISION OF TWO FRACTIONS (1/4, 1/2, 2/3, 3/4, 4/5, 5/6)

4 ⋯⋯ ● Pentagon Score (page 84)
COMBINATION OF ADDITION, SUBTRACTION, AND MULTIPLICATION OF THREE NUMBERS (0–9)

✔ **Smile Squares** (page 89)
✔ **Spinners B and D** (pages 87–88)
✔ **Dice A and B** (page 93)
✔ **resealable plastic bags**

‹‹ Directions

1 Photocopy a set of Smile Squares and a spinner or dice for each game board. Cut apart the Smile Squares, and assemble the spinners and dice. Place each set of materials in a bag.

2 Give a group of two or three students a reproducible at the appropriate level and a bag of materials.

3 Have players, in turn, spin the spinner twice or roll the dice; add, subtract, multiply, or divide (depending on the game) the two numbers; and cover their answer with a Smile Square.

4 Have players record 1 point for each already covered space on the game board that is connected (horizontally, vertically, or diagonally) to the space they just covered.

5 Tell players that if they spin or roll and are unable to cover a number, they lose their turn. If a number *could* have been covered, any player can cover the space and score points.

6 When a player cannot cover a number in three successive turns, he or she is out of the game. The game ends when all players are out or when all numbers are covered. The player with the most points is the winner.

Helpful Hints

➤ Have students who are playing Hexagon Score and Pentagon Score use scratch paper to work out their problems.

➤ Invite students to play a variation of the game in which they only score 1 point if an opponent's Smile Square covers the connected space. (Photocopy Smile Squares on different colored paper to distinguish players' game pieces.)

Square Score

Directions

- Roll a **pair of Die A.** Add or subtract the two numbers. Find the answer on the game board. Cover it with a Smile Square.

- You score 1 point for each covered square that is connected (horizontally, vertically, or diagonally) to the square you covered.

- If you cannot cover a number, you lose your turn. If a number *could* have been covered, any player can cover it and score points.

- You are out of the game when you cannot cover a number for three turns in a row. The game ends when all players are out or when all of the numbers are covered. The player with the most points is the winner.

Add or subtract to score more!

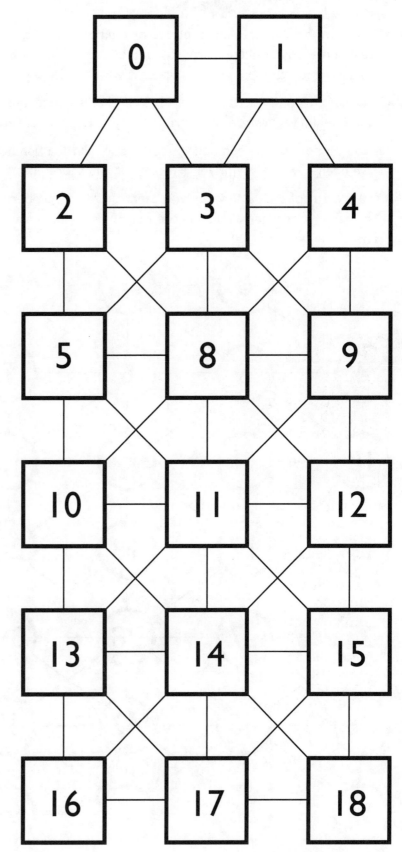

Multilevel Math Fun • 3–5 © 2002 Creative Teaching Press

Circle Score

Directions

- Spin **Spinner B** twice. Add, subtract, or multiply the two numbers. For example, if your two numbers are 4 and 3, you could perform any one of these operations: $4 + 3 = 7$, $4 - 3 = 1$, or $4 \times 3 = 12$. Find the answer on the game board. Cover it with a Smile Square.

- You score 1 point for each covered circle that is connected (horizontally, vertically, or diagonally) to the circle you covered.

- If you cannot cover a number, you lose your turn. If a number *could* have been covered, any player can cover it and score points.

- You are out of the game when you cannot cover a number for three turns in a row. The game ends when all players are out or when all of the numbers are covered. The player with the most points is the winner.

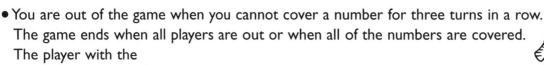

Score more with addition, subtraction, or multiplication!

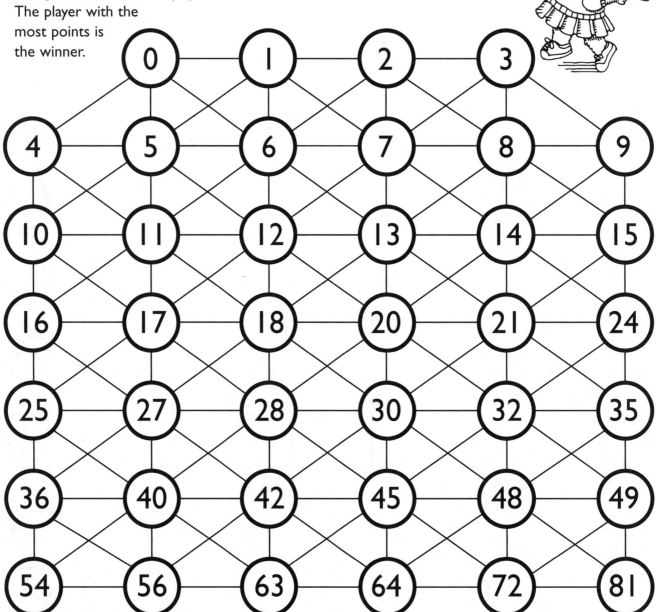

Multilevel Math Fun • 3–5 © 2002 Creative Teaching Press

Hexagon Score

Multilevel Math Fun • 3–5 © 2002 Creative Teaching Press

Directions

- Spin **Spinner D** twice. Add, subtract, multiply, or divide the two fractions. For example, if your two fractions are $\frac{1}{4}$ and $\frac{1}{2}$ you could perform any one of these operations: $\frac{1}{4} + \frac{1}{2} = \frac{3}{4}$, $\frac{1}{2} - \frac{1}{4} = \frac{1}{4}$, $\frac{1}{4} \times \frac{1}{2} = \frac{1}{8}$, or $\frac{1}{4} \div \frac{1}{2} = \frac{1}{2}$. Find the answer on the game board. Cover it with a Smile Square.

- You score 1 point for each covered hexagon that is connected (horizontally, vertically, or diagonally) to the hexagon you covered.

- If you cannot cover a fraction, you lose your turn. If a fraction *could* have been covered, any player can cover it and score points.

- You are out of the game when you cannot cover a fraction for three turns in a row. The game ends when all players are out or when all of the fractions are covered. The player with the most points is the winner.

Pentagon Score

Directions

- Roll **three Die Bs.** Add, subtract, multiply, or combine these operations for the three numbers rolled. For example, if your three numbers are 1, 3, and 4, you could perform any one of the operations or a combination of them: $1 + 3 + 4 = 8$, $4 - 3 - 1 = 0$, $1 \times 3 \times 4 = 12$, or $1 \times 3 + 4 = 7$. Find the answer on the game board. Cover it with a Smile Square.

- You score 1 point for each covered pentagon that is connected (horizontally, vertically, or diagonally) to the pentagon you covered.

- If you cannot cover a number, you lose your turn. If a number *could* have been covered, any player can cover it and score points.

- You are out of the game when you cannot cover a number for three turns in a row. The game ends when all players are out or when all of the numbers are covered. The player with the most points is the winner.

Combine addition, subtraction, and multiplication.

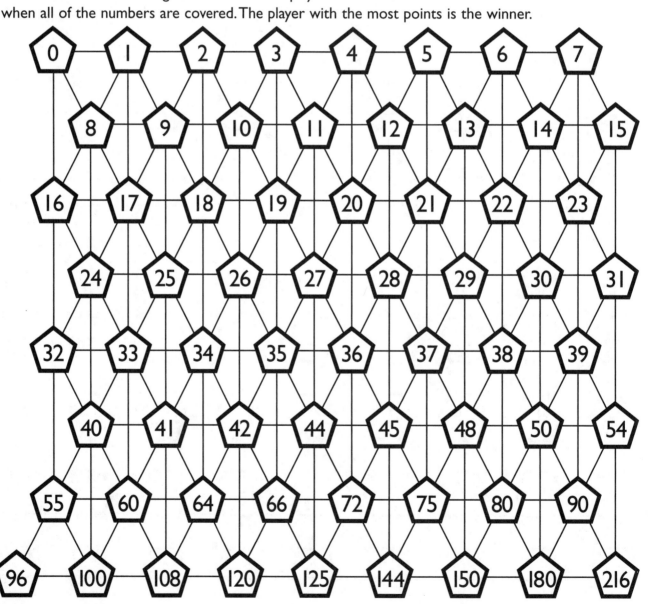

Multilevel Math Fun • 3–5 © 2002 Creative Teaching Press

Hundred Board

1	2	3	4	5	6	7	8	9	10
11	12	13	14	15	16	17	18	19	20
21	22	23	24	25	26	27	28	29	30
31	32	33	34	35	36	37	38	39	40
41	42	43	44	45	46	47	48	49	50
51	52	53	54	55	56	57	58	59	60
61	62	63	64	65	66	67	68	69	70
71	72	73	74	75	76	77	78	79	80
81	82	83	84	85	86	87	88	89	90
91	92	93	94	95	96	97	98	99	100

Use with
• Number Puzzles (pages 27–31)

0	**1**	**2**	$\dfrac{1}{10}$	$\dfrac{7}{10}$
3	**4**	**5**	$\dfrac{2}{10}$	$\dfrac{8}{10}$
6	**7**	**8**	$\dfrac{3}{10}$	$\dfrac{9}{10}$
0.3	**0.4**	**0.5**	$\dfrac{4}{10}$	
0.6	**0.7**	**0.8**	$\dfrac{5}{10}$	
0.9	**1.0**	**1.1**	$\dfrac{6}{10}$	

Multilevel Math Fun • 3–5 © 2002 Creative Teaching Press

Spinners

Photocopy on card stock, laminate, and cut out each spinner. Write *Spinner A* or *Spinner B* on the back. Put a brass fastener through the end of a paper clip, and push the fastener through the center of the spinner.

Spinner A

Use with
• Spin Big! (pages 47–51)

Spinner B

Use with
• Frame It (pages 57–61)
• Target the Frog (page 68)
• Target the Fish (page 71)
• Circle Score (page 82)

Spinners

Photocopy on card stock, laminate, and cut out each spinner. Write *Spinner C* or *Spinner D* on the back. Put a brass fastener through the end of a paper clip, and push the fastener through the center of the spinner.

Spinner C

Use with
- Target the Dolphin (page 69)
- Target the Turtle (page 70)

Spinner C wheel: 1, 2, 3, 4, 5, 6, 7, 8, 9, 10

Spinner D

Use with
- Hexagon Score (page 83)

Spinner D wheel: 1/4, 1/2, 2/3, 3/4, 4/5, 5/6

Multilevel Math Fun • 3–5 © 2002 Creative Teaching Press

Smile Squares

Photocopy the Smile Squares on card stock, and then cut them apart. Store each set in a plastic bag.

Use with
• Factor It (pages 62–66)
• Score More (pages 80–84)

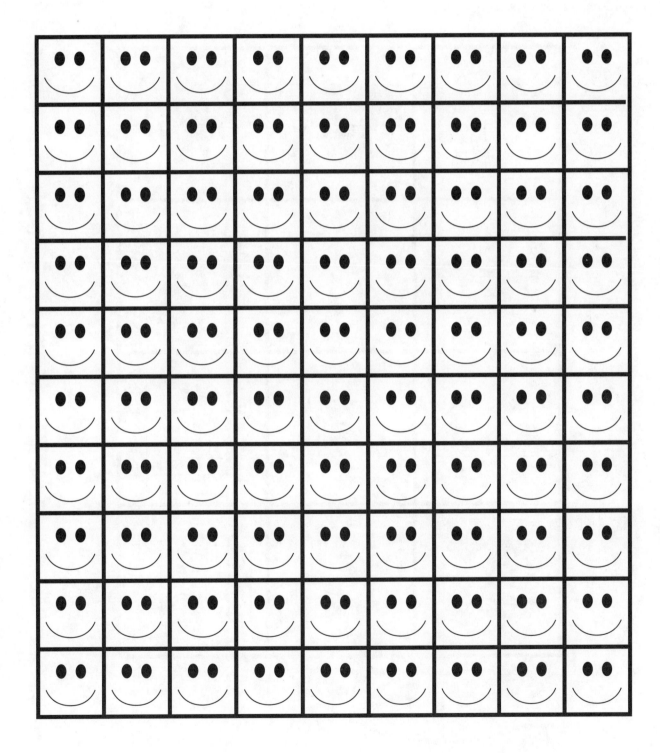

Fraction Cards

Set A

Use with

- Fractions in a Row (pages 77–79)

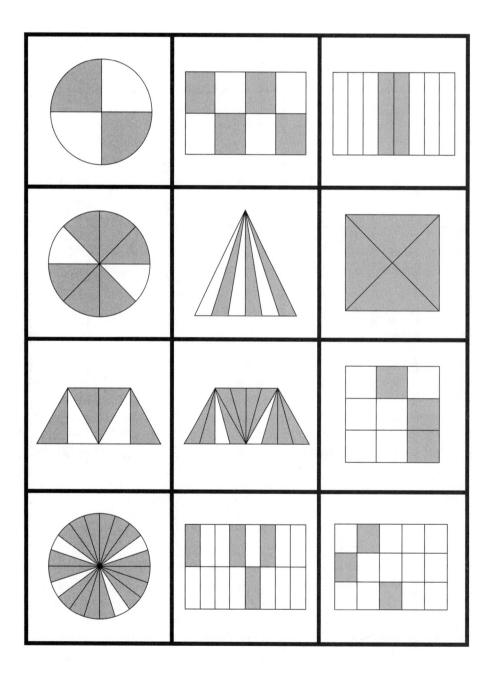

Multilevel Math Fun • 3–5 © 2002 Creative Teaching Press

Set B

Use with

• Fractions in a Row (pages 77–79)

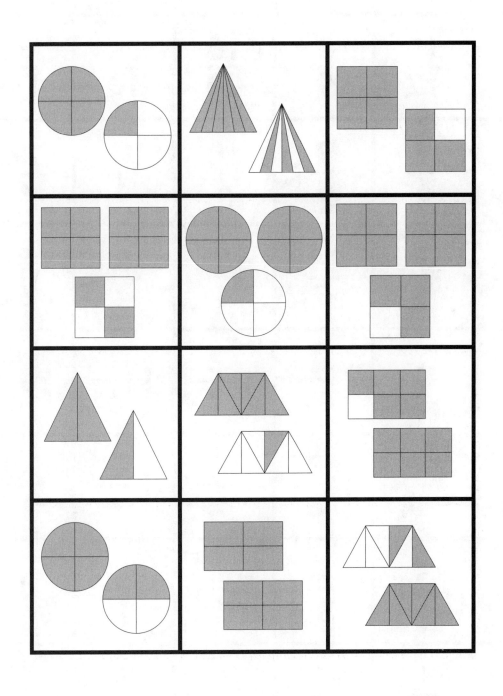

Fraction Caller Cards

$\dfrac{2}{4}$	$\dfrac{4}{8}$	$\dfrac{2}{8}$	$\dfrac{6}{8}$	$\dfrac{3}{6}$	$\dfrac{4}{4}$
$\dfrac{4}{6}$	$\dfrac{10}{12}$	$\dfrac{3}{9}$	$\dfrac{16}{20}$	$\dfrac{4}{16}$	$\dfrac{3}{15}$
$\dfrac{5}{4}$	$\dfrac{9}{6}$	$\dfrac{7}{4}$	$\dfrac{10}{4}$	$\dfrac{9}{4}$	$\dfrac{11}{4}$
$\dfrac{3}{2}$	$\dfrac{7}{6}$	$\dfrac{11}{6}$	$\dfrac{6}{4}$	$\dfrac{8}{4}$	$\dfrac{8}{6}$
$1\dfrac{1}{2}$	2	$1\dfrac{1}{4}$	$1\dfrac{3}{4}$	$1\dfrac{1}{6}$	$1\dfrac{5}{6}$
$2\dfrac{1}{4}$	$2\dfrac{3}{4}$	$1\dfrac{3}{6}$	$1\dfrac{2}{4}$	$1\dfrac{2}{6}$	$2\dfrac{2}{4}$
$\dfrac{1}{2}$	$\dfrac{4}{5}$	$\dfrac{1}{4}$	$\dfrac{3}{4}$	$\dfrac{1}{3}$	1
$\dfrac{2}{3}$	$\dfrac{1}{2}$	$\dfrac{5}{6}$	$\dfrac{1}{5}$	$\dfrac{1}{2}$	$\dfrac{1}{4}$

Set A: Use with Fractions, Fractions rules sheet and Fraction Cards Set A

Set B: Use with Improper Fractions rules sheet and Fraction Cards Set B

Set C: Use with Mixed Number Fractions rules sheet and Fraction Cards Set B

Set D: Use with Reduce the Fractions rules sheet and Fraction Cards Set A

Multilevel Math Fun • 3–5 © 2002 Creative Teaching Press

Photocopy on card stock, laminate, and cut out each die. Fold on the dotted lines, and glue the sides together.

Die A

Use with
• Square Score (page 81)

Die B

Use with
• Pentagon Score (page 84)

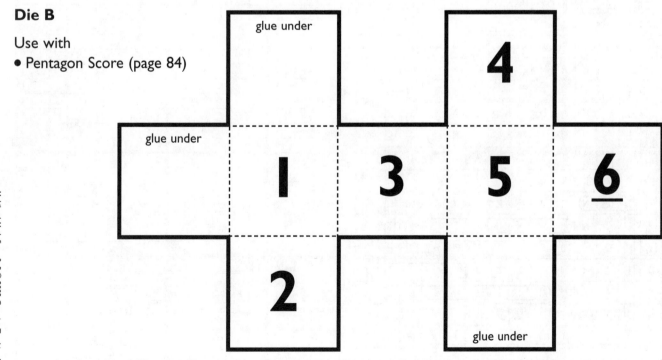

Multilevel Math Fun • 3–5 © 2002 Creative Teaching Press

Answers

Page 13

```
A  B  N  F  C  S  U  M  S  B
W  K  U  A  J  F  D  I  O  P
D  V  M  C  F  R  S  R  L  R
S  U  B  T  R  A  C  T  V  O
L  G  E  O  H  C  Q  P  E  B
Y  U  R  R  A  T  I  O  A  L
Q  L  F  S  D  I  V  I  D  E
U  A  G  T  D  O  K  W  M
O  N  T  I  I  N  D  F  B  E
T  S  E  M  T  Y  D  N  C  Q
I  W  S  U  I  C  X  J  Z  U
E  E  P  R  O  D  U  C  T  A
N  R  Q  H  N  P  G  M  O  L
T  M  U  L  T  I  P  L  Y  S
```

Page 14

```
Z  E  R  O  N  V  Q  U  A  R  T  E  R  F
A  R  P  B  Q  U  B  I  L  L  I  O  N  E
H  D  D  L  C  F  M  F  I  N  H  T  T  E
U  C  C  P  A  H  Z  E  O  S  J  H  H  R
N  E  O  T  G  C  S  S  R  M  D  I  O  T
D  S  M  M  W  U  E  V  O  A  K  R  U  H
R  C  P  E  M  I  P  V  S  N  L  D  O
E  B  A  B  V  A  C  Z  A  W  M  I  A  U
D  P  R  K  R  U  T  Q  T  L  J  O  N  S
T  T  E  N  P  P  R  M  P  Y  U  N  D  A
H  E  Z  A  H  U  N  D  R  E  D  E  T  N
S  N  O  L  D  E  C  I  M  A  L  S  H
D  T  Z  X  N  C  T  D  I  G  I  T  S  Y
F  H  A  E  U  M  I  L  L  I  O  N  S  A
C  S  Y  V  G  D  U  Z  L  J  K  H  O  N
H  A  L  F  N  U  M  B  E  R  M  G  W
```

Page 15

```
A  E  C  D  Y  W  D  I  F  F  E  R  E  N  C  E  P
B  E  Q  U  A  T  I  O  N  A  X  E  N  P  F  C  X
K  T  U  S  B  B  G  D  D  E  C  I  M  A  L  O  M
V  G  Y  M  U  D  I  V  I  D  E  N  D  Z  G  M  M
A  E  G  U  R  M  T  A  M  H  I  J  I  D  H  P  P
Z  P  R  O  B  A  B  I  L  I  T  Y  U  U  U  P  E
H  O  F  P  G  X  C  L  Q  U  O  T  I  E  N  T  Z
I  S  H  P  R  I  M  E  A  A  P  O  S  V  D  A  E
J  I  S  O  M  V  W  Q  P  T  Z  M  I  B  R  T  O
L  T  R  S  T  W  N  O  S  R  O  Z  O  M  E  I  R
I  I  D  I  V  I  S  O  R  O  M  T  N  I  D  O  Y
H  V  G  T  Q  F  F  N  E  G  A  T  I  V  E  N  L
X  E  D  E  N  O  M  I  N  A  T  O  R  L  T  K  Q
U  T  H  O  U  S  A  N  D  E  F  I  L  D  V  I  S
V  O  O  M  B  O  S  I  I  B  R  E  S  T  R  K  D
A  D  E  M  A  N  I  P  U  L  A  T  I  V  E  J  R
K  M  A  A  G  O  B  S  S  U  C  F  V  G  M  H  T
M  U  L  T  I  P  L  I  C  A  T  I  O  N  A  C  B
C  L  G  H  B  E  Q  U  A  L  I  D  L  F  I  B  G
S  T  E  N  O  R  C  Z  K  V  O  Q  W  N  R  O  U
R  I  B  D  Z  C  W  M  A  T  N  S  I  P  D  N  H
C  P  R  A  F  E  S  T  I  M  A  T  E  S  E  B  J
D  L  A  B  A  N  O  O  N  V  L  M  K  Q  R  W  V
E  E  W  X  G  T  H  Y  J  K  Y  R  O  T  C  A  F
```

Page 16

```
T  C  A  F  B  G  E  O  M  E  T  R  Y  M  N  O  N
R  H  O  M  B  U  S  I  K  G  R  A  P  H  P  R  T
A  O  E  A  B  L  D  H  I  J  I  S  A  E  R  A  O
P  R  D  A  C  G  B  S  T  P  A  W  X  X  A  B  C
E  D  E  U  C  S  Q  P  L  A  N  E  P  A  X  I  S
Z  S  E  V  W  U  B  V  R  U  G  E  G  G  Q  D  P
O  T  F  W  A  T  J  E  P  T  L  F  S  O  L  I  D
I  E  D  R  S  R  T  C  U  B  E  O  R  N  S  K  E
D  F  E  Y  T  E  G  I  X  F  O  Z  N  G  M  L  D
E  G  E  F  M  F  B  R  Z  Y  N  T  R  P  S  T  K
R  F  T  A  G  H  O  C  E  N  T  E  R  R  A  Y  T
C  D  I  E  E  X  A  L  M  M  Y  K  L  I  N  E  U
A  D  R  Y  M  A  N  E  Y  N  U  J  L  S  I  D  E
H  P  A  R  A  L  L  E  L  O  G  R  A  M  B  T  M
Y  Y  Q  A  B  C  P  Y  X  C  Z  H  W  B  J  V  U
T  A  N  B  Q  I  M  U  N  A  I  C  W  B  O  C
I  M  G  H  P  E  N  T  A  G  O  N  A  D  O  D  V
A  L  R  K  C  L  L  H  O  G  E  X  N  L  L  C
P  D  E  S  E  G  M  E  N  T  D  E  E  W  G  O
A  A  I  U  E  T  A  F  G  S  S  P  H  E  R  E  N
C  O  O  R  D  I  N  A  T  E  L  N  L  M  N  O  P
C  K  Q  R  S  J  O  P  C  K  O  P  R  A  U  V  V
F  B  C  E  H  I  L  S  T  A  P  Q  E  B  F  M  D
G  Q  U  A  D  R  I  L  A  T  E  R  A  L  C  G  H
```

Answers

Page 18
10

Page 19
2.5

Page 20
⁻1

Page 21
$11\frac{9}{8}$ or $14\frac{7}{8}$

Page 23

1. + −
2. x ÷
3. + −
   or x ÷
4. − ÷
5. ÷ −

6. − −
7. x −
8. x x
   or x ÷
9. x −
10. ÷ +

Page 24

1. x −
2. x + +
3. x
4. ÷
5. ÷

6. +
7. ÷ + −
8. − +
9. x x −
10. + −

Page 25

1. + + −
2. + x ÷
3. x x
4. x x +
5. x ÷ ÷
   or ÷ x ÷

6. − x
7. + x −
8. x + or x −
9. x x x
10. + + ÷
   or x − ÷

Page 26

1. + −
2. + − +
3. x x ÷
4. x + x +
5. ÷ x

6. + + +
7. − −
8. + +
9. + x
10. + x or + −

Page 28

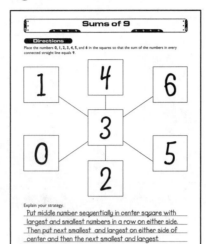

Page 29

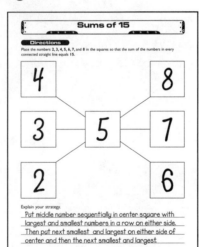

Page 30

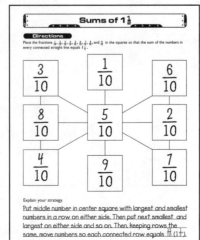

Page 31

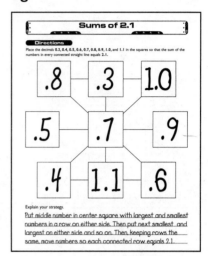

Page 33

Page 34

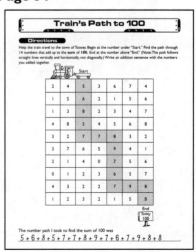

Page 35

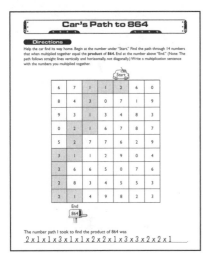

Page 36

Page 38

1. 5
2. 9
3. 11
4. 5
5. 18

6. 4
7. 13
8. 40
9. 28
10. 13

Page 39

1. 1
2. 21
3. 999
4. 10
5. ⁴/₁₈ or ²/₉

6. 6
7. 99
8. 2
9. 74
10. 41

Page 40

1. 3
2. ²⁰/₆ or 3²/₆ or 3¹/₃
3. 6
4. ⁸/₁₈ or ⁴/₉
5. ²/₈ or ¹/₄

6. 1,230
7. 6
8. 3
9. 31
10. 92

Page 41

1. 11.61
2. ²/₃
3. ⁷/₁₆
4. 0.31
5. 84

6. 41
7. 15
8. 661
9. ⁻515
10. ⁻47

Page 43

Page 44

Page 45

Page 46

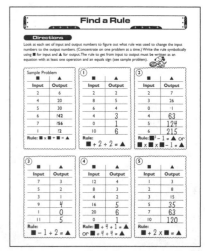